SCIENCE PLUS+

THIRD EDITION

G000135188

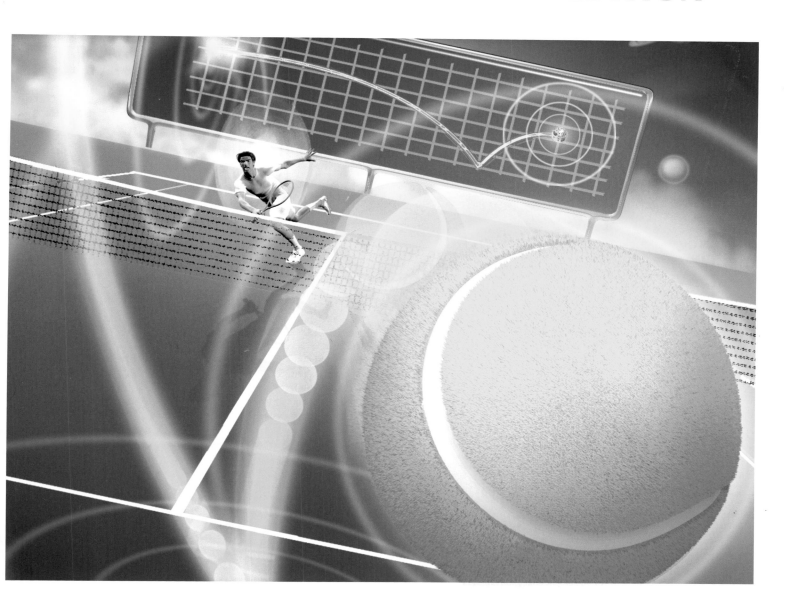

1

William Collins' dream of knowledge for all began with the publication of his first book in 1819. A self-educated mill worker, he not only enriched millions of lives, but also founded a flourishing publishing house. Today, staying true to this spirit, Collins books are packed with inspiration, innovation and practical expertise. They place you at the centre of a world of possibility and give you exactly what you need to explore it.

Collins. Freedom to teach.

Published by Collins
An imprint of HarperCollins*Publishers*
77–85 Fulham Palace Road
Hammersmith
London
W6 8JB

Browse the complete Collins catalogue at
www.collinseducation.com

© HarperCollins*Publishers* Limited 2006

10 9 8 7 6 5 4 3 2 1

ISBN 0 00 721648 3

Gareth Price asserts his moral right to be identified as the author of this work

British Library Cataloguing in Publication Data
A Catalogue record for this publication is available from the British Library

Commissioned by Kate Hayward and Cassandra Birmingham

Publishing Manager Michael Cotter

Project managed by Jennifer Carruth

Edited by Anita Clark

Proofread by Philippa Boxer

Cover design by John Fordham and Bob Lea

Internal design by JPD

Page make-up by JPD

Picture research by Caroline Thompson

Illustrations by IFADesign Ltd and JPD

Production by Natasha Buckland

Printed and bound in Hong Kong by Printing Express Ltd

Acknowledgements

Every effort has been made to contact the holders of copyright material, but if any have been inadvertently overlooked the publishers will be pleased to make the necessary arrangements at the first opportunity.

The publishers would like to thank the following for permission to reproduce photographs (T = Top, B = Bottom, C = Centre, L= Left, R = Right):

Action Plus/E Escoffier, p74, Glyn Kirk, p86;
Alamy Images/Sindre Ellingsen, p112;
Ardea London Ltd/Doc White, p20TL;
Martyn Chillmaid, p51, p54L, p58R, p94TCR,T,CL&B, p113B, p127BL&C;
Corbis/Galen Rowell, p52L, Jon Hicks, p66, James Sparshatt, p67, Owen Franken, p68, Lester Lefkowitz, p95, Jean Miele, p126T;
Empics/PA, p43T;
Getty Images/Stone, p29CL, p107B, Photographer's Choice, p82, Taxi, p101T, p110;
Michael Holford, p58L&C, p64TR;
Illustration © Karen Carr, p19C;
iStockphoto, p5, p16C, p19T, p25, p26, 28TR&CR, p29TR, p30TR, p34, p35, p40, p42, p47, p55, p64R, p65, p115T;
© 2006 JupiterImages Corporation, p14, p24;
Courtesy the Kobal Collection/Universal, p4, p73T, p97, United Artists, p7, Amblin Universal, p16T, Icon/Ladd Co/Paramount, p46TL, Tri-Star, p73C, Hal Roach/MGM, p76, Danjaq/Eon/UA/Hamshere, Keith, p88, Dimension Films, p114;
Andrew Lambert Photographic Collection, p48;
M-dash.com/Martin Wilson, 119BR;
Jef Maion/Nomads'Land, p38;
Mary Evans Picture Library, p17CL, p19CL;
Marc Merlin/http://marc.merlins.org/perso/bm/, p98, p109, p124;
Mountain Camera Picture Library/Leo Dickinson, p71;
NASA, p52R;
NASA Jet Propulsion Laboratory (NASA-JPL), p118;
OSF/Thomas Haider, p20TR, David B Fleetham, p20CL;
Photofusion/Libby Welch, p12;
photolibrary.com/Index Stock, p125;
Popperfoto.com, p46TR;
Gareth Price, p8, p30TL, p32, p53, p56, p64L, p80, p85, p89, p90, p91, p94BCR, p101C, p102B, p104, p116B, p119CL, p126L, p127T, p128;
Redferns/David Redfern, p41;
Rex Features Ltd, p11, p37, p107T, Lee Smith, p6, Anders Krusberg, p20CR, SHOUT, p22, David Levenson, p28TL, Nils Jorgensen, p31, Crispin Thruston, p54T, Sipa Press, p59, p60, p77, p108, Charles Knight, p61, Tony Kyriacou, p70, Arnold Slater, p103, Richard Young, p113T, Brian Rasic, p116T, Steve Mayes, p119T, Novastock, p120;
Science Photo Library/Mark Garlick, p17T, Klaus Guldbrandsen, p23, Dept. of Clinical Radiology, Salisbury District Hospital, p43C, David M Martin. MD, p49TL, Mehau Kulyk, p78, David Hay, p79, David Parker, p83, Francoise Sauze, p84, George Bernard, p92, AJ Photo/Hop American, p100, Pekka Parviainen, p101B, Martin Bond, p102T, Nasa, p106, p122, Manfred Kage, p115B, Planetary Visions Ltd, p121, Cordelia Molloy, p127BR;
© SHOUT, p72;
John Sibbick, p17CR;
C&S Thompson, p49TR;
Topfoto, Image Works, p62;
Woodfall Wild Images/David Woodfall, p49C.

Additional photos by Gareth Price

Biology

Chemistry

Physics

Contents

1.1 The undead?

What are the seven life processes?

How do you know something is alive? Can you tell just by looking or do you need complicated machines and years of training?

When people are alive they **breathe**, their blood **circulates**, they **grow**, they **move**, they eat, **digest** and **excrete** food. They may **reproduce** and they **respond** to changes around them. All these things that living people do are called **life processes**. If the body is not doing any of these things you can guess that the person is dead.

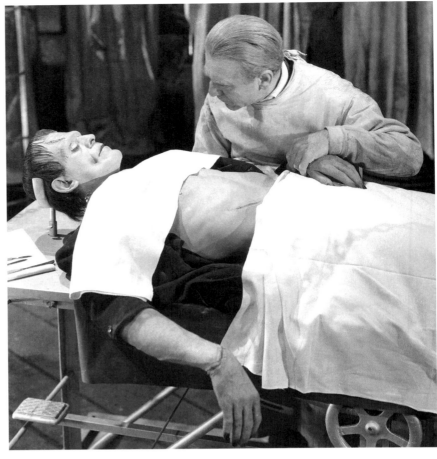

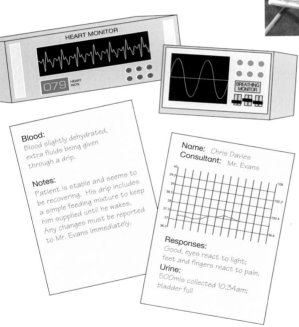

HEART MONITOR

079 HEART RATE

BREATHING MONITOR

Blood:
Blood slightly dehydrated, extra fluids being given through a drip.

Notes:
Patient is stable and seems to be recovering. His drip includes a simple feeding mixture to keep him supplied until he wakes. Any changes must be reported to Mr. Evans immediately.

Name: Chris Davies
Consultant: Mr. Evans

Responses:
Good, eyes react to light; feet and fingers react to pain.
Urine:
500mls collected 10.34am; bladder full

The body system	The main organs	Important life process
Respiratory	Lungs	Breathe
Circulatory	Heart and blood vessels	Circulate blood
Digestive	Stomach and intestines	Digest food
Excretory	Kidneys	Filter waste products from the blood
Reproductive	Ovaries and testes	Produce babies

Keywords

breathe

circulate

grow

move

digest

excrete

reproduce

respond

life process

Questions

1 List seven things that tell you a person is alive.

2 What does the information on the medical chart above tell you about Chris Davies' condition?

3 List *all* the processes that go on in a living body.

4 How can you tell that each process is working?

5 How can you tell that plants are alive?

Dead or alive?

1.2 Visitors from the stars?

 Which organs can we transplant?

An alien spaceship crash-lands in a mysterious airbase in the USA. The ship contains three aliens. They are not moving. Are they dead? If we find the same life processes and body parts as in humans we can assume they are still alive.

Different parts of the body do different jobs. Doctors can remove some damaged body parts and replace them. A metal pin in your leg can do the job of a bone. Some people have an artificial heart made of steel and plastic beating in their chest.

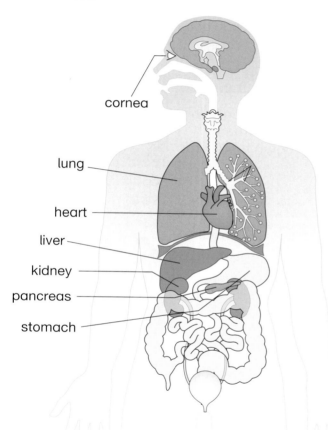

- cornea
- lung
- heart
- liver
- kidney
- pancreas
- stomach

Some people are willing for their organs to be transplanted after they die. These people are called **donors**. After we die organs in our body can be **transplanted** into another person. The person who gets the organs is called the **host**. Hosts need to match the donors. This stops the host's body **rejecting** the new organ.

But when we die our bodies start to **decay**. After a short while it cannot be used for transplants. Doctors often keep the body cool to reduce the speed of decay.

Donor organ	Cannot be used after
heart	7 hours
liver	7 hours
pancreas	30 hours
kidney	72 hours

Questions

1 List six body parts that can be transplanted.
2 How are the removed organs kept in good condition?
3 What does the word **donor** mean?
4 Which organ lasts the longest after the death of the donor?
5 Write down three problems with transplant operations.
6 The victim was murdered with a bread knife to the heart at breakfast (8:00 am). His body was found at 6:00 pm the same day. Which organs could still be transplanted?

Keywords

donor

transplant

host

rejection

decay

1.3 We are the champions!

 How do we get energy to live?

Liverpool won the Champions League in 2005. Does your team ever win anything?

Footballers' **energy** comes from the food that they eat. The body **respires** sugar in the food to release energy to move the muscles. **Respiration** uses **oxygen** and gives out **carbon dioxide** as waste.

$$\textbf{Glucose} + \textbf{oxygen} \rightarrow \textbf{carbon dioxide} + \textbf{water} + \textbf{energy}$$

During a football match the players need more energy. To get more energy they need more oxygen. They **breathe** more deeply and their hearts beats faster. The faster **heartbeat** pushes blood around the body more quickly. Blood carries oxygen from the lungs to the busy muscles.

After the match their heart rate and breathing slow down to resting levels. Very fit athletes **recover** much more quickly than unfit people.

Before exercising it is sensible to warm up. This increases blood flow to the muscles to prevent muscle damage during very strenuous exercise. After finishing the match it is good to cool down gently for the same reason.

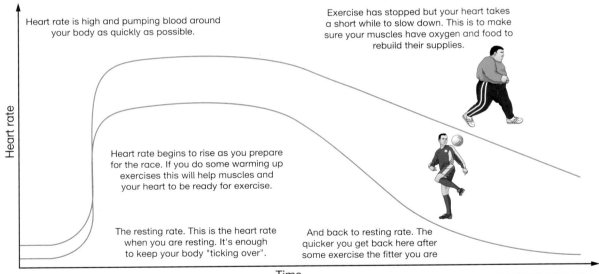

Heart rate is high and pumping blood around your body as quickly as possible.

Exercise has stopped but your heart takes a short while to slow down. This is to make sure your muscles have oxygen and food to rebuild their supplies.

Heart rate begins to rise as you prepare for the race. If you do some warming up exercises this will help muscles and your heart to be ready for exercise.

The resting rate. This is the heart rate when you are resting. It's enough to keep your body "ticking over".

And back to resting rate. The quicker you get back here after some exercise the fitter you are

Heart rate

Time

Questions

1 What happens to your heart rate when you start exercising?
2 What does your body do to food to get the energy out?
3 List two substances produced by respiration.
4 How does oxygen get to the muscles in a footballer's legs?
5 Give two differences between the graphs showing the heart rates of the footballer and the fan.
6 Why does warming up seem to help muscles work better?

Keywords

energy

respire

respiration

oxygen

carbon dioxide

breathe

heartbeat

recovery

1.4 The reanimator

Why are cells damaged by freezing?

The low temperature in this coffin will preserve Dracula – if he wasn't already one of the undead! Some people have their bodies frozen when they die. They hope that science will be able to bring them back to life in the future. Some have their heads frozen. They want a new body when they are revived.

We cool food and body organs to slow down the speed of decay. But frozen food is not the same as fresh food. Why?

Bodies are built of **cells**. There are roughly 75 million, million cells in each of us! There are many different types of cell. These cells look very different but they all have a **nucleus**, **cytoplasm** and a **cell membrane**.

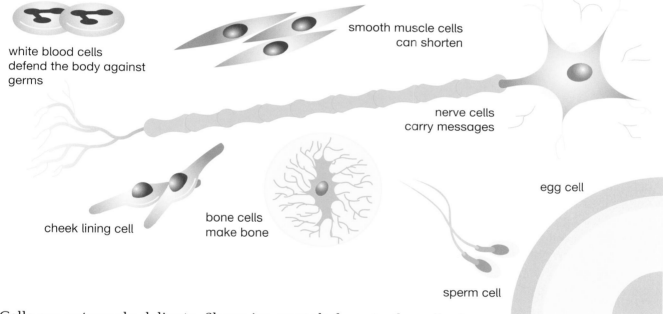

white blood cells defend the body against germs

smooth muscle cells can shorten

nerve cells carry messages

cheek lining cell

bone cells make bone

egg cell

sperm cell

Cells are extremely delicate. Sharp ice crystals form in the cell when it freezes. The crystals burst the membrane. Freezing cells is difficult. Freezing whole bodies must be even harder!

Questions

1 What is a cell?

2 Draw and label a cell.

3 Name three human cells and say what they do.

4 What are some of the problems with trying to freeze cells?

5 Draw diagrams to show what happens when a cell freezes.

6 Plan an investigation to find out if slow freezing or fast freezing does the most damage to cells.

Keywords

cell

nucleus

cytoplasm

cell membrane

1 Data response: **Organ transplants**

'My name is Daphne. I was very ill when I was 10 and my kidneys were damaged. I spent 3 years on a kidney dialysis machine. In 2003 I was given a kidney from someone who had been killed in a road accident. It changed my life. I am doing a project for my GCSE about kidney transplants. I asked all of my friends and family what they thought about organ donors. These are my results.'

Doctors can take organs from donors:

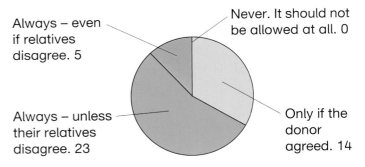

Always – even if relatives disagree. 5

Never. It should not be allowed at all. 0

Always – unless their relatives disagree. 23

Only if the donor agreed. 14

At the moment people carry a donor card if they want their organs to be used after they have died. This is called the 'opt in system'. Should doctors have the right to collect organs unless people have said that they do not want to give them? This is the 'opt out system'.

Transplants in the UK since 2000

Year	Number of transplants	People waiting for transplants	Number of donors
2000	1393	4786	741
2001	1359	4927	731
2002	1313	4970	705
2003	1399	5020	743
2004	1386	5074	735

data from NHS Transplant Group 2005

Data response

1 How many people thought doctors should be able to get organs from donors even if their relatives disagreed?

2 How many people did Daphne ask in her survey?

3 How many people in Daphne's survey agreed with the 'opt in' system for organ donors?

4 Do you think Daphne's survey was fair? Might her results be biased?

5 Give a reason for your answer to question 4.

6 Is the number of people waiting for transplants going up or down?

7   Carry out some research to find one reason why transplants are difficult to do. In your answer say where you found your information.

8   A government minister is considering changing the current 'opt in' system for organ donation. Find three useful pieces of information for the minister. Say where you found your information.

9   You work for a charity that campaigns to encourage more people to become organ donors. Design a poster or prepare a short radio advert to highlight the advantages and disadvantages of both the 'opt in' and 'opt out' systems.

Learning progress

I know:

- The life processes are growth, digestion, reproduction, movement, sensitivity, excretion, and breathing.
- The circulatory system moves blood carrying food and oxygen around the body.
- The respiratory system swaps carbon dioxide for oxygen in the lungs.
- The digestive system breaks down foods so that they can be absorbed into the body.
- The position of the lungs, heart, kidneys, liver, brain and stomach in a diagram.
- The nucleus controls the cell. The membrane allows some chemicals to pass in and out. Useful chemical reactions take place in the cytoplasm.
- The position of the nucleus, cytoplasm and cell membrane in a diagram of an animal cell.
- Exercise needs energy, and lack of energy causes tiredness or muscle cramp. Cells use oxygen to release energy from glucose (sugar). This is called respiration.
- A person's breathing rate and pulse rate can be measured.
- Fit people tend to recover more quickly after exercise than unfit people and it is possible to measure how quickly a person recovers from exercise. Warming up and cooling down helps to reduce muscle damage during exercise.
- Some healthy organs can be removed from dead people and transplanted into hosts. People can opt to donate their organs and can carry donor cards. Cooling slows down decay but freezing can damage cells.

I can:

- Measure a person's breathing rate/pulse.
- Measure how fast a person recovers from exercise.
- Work out a simple 10 minute fitness programme.

Respond • Research • Present

2.1 Reproductive organs

 What are the reproductive organs?

The parts of the male and female reproductive systems that we can see outside the body are called **genitals**. Other body structures are also needed to produce babies. These are called reproductive organs.

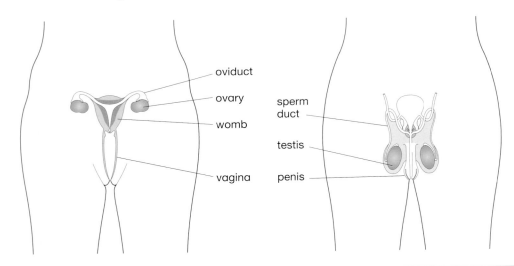

Reproductive organ	Function
Ovary	Produces the egg. Waves of fluid carry the egg along the oviduct to the womb.
Oviduct	A tube that carries the egg from the ovary to the womb. The sperm **fertilises** the egg in the oviduct.
Womb	A muscular bag where the baby develops before birth. Also called the uterus.
Vagina	Connects the uterus to the outside of the body.
Testis	Produces **sperm** cells.
Sperm duct	A tube that carries sperm from the testis to the penis.
Penis	Becomes hard and can place sperm in the vagina of the female. The sperm then swim up to the oviduct.

The male releases most of the sperm in a rush during an **ejaculation**. However, some sperm leaks out before this. Even this small amount of sperm can lead to a baby if it enters the vagina.

Keywords

genitals

ovary

oviduct

fertilise

womb

vagina

testis

sperm

sperm duct

penis

ejaculation

Questions

1 Which part of the man produces sperm?

2 Which part of the woman produces the egg?

3 Where do the sperm and egg meet?

4 What happens when the sperm fertilises the egg?

5 Why can a woman become pregnant even if the man does not ejaculate in her vagina?

Babies

2.2　A pause for pregnancy

 Why do doctors carry out antenatal tests?

Katie Price, better known as Jordan, carrying Peter Andre's baby.

When a woman becomes **pregnant** her periods stop and she begins to gain weight. She will probably go to an **antenatal** clinic. Antenatal means 'before birth'.

The staff at the antenatal clinic look after the mother and monitor the development of the unborn baby. They check the mother's **blood pressure**, **weight** and **height** and test her urine for chemicals which might show that the baby is in trouble.

Sometimes the mother will visit hospital for an ultrasound scan. This can show if she is carrying twins. Identical twins are formed right at the start of pregnancy when one fertilised egg splits into two.

Once the baby has been born, the mother begins to lose the weight she has gained and her periods start again.

DATE OF CONFINEMENT...... _8/6/05_
PREGNANCY MATURITY...... _40+6_ ......WEEKS
LABOUR 1st stage........ _12hrs 45mins_
　　　　2nd stage........ _1hr 40mins_
　　　　3rd stage........ _5mins_
TOTAL DURATION..... _14hrs 30mins_
METHOD OF DELIVERY
　Placenta and membranes complete
　Blood loss 300mls.
SEX: (MALE) FEMALE　(ring as appropriate)
BIRTH MASS........... _3350_ .....g
DISCHARGE MASS...... _3600_ .....g
METHOD OF FEEDING......... _Breast_
POST NATAL CARE HOSPITAL /(GP)

PREFERRED HOSPITAL...........................
PREFERRED CONSULTANT...................

Date	Last period (weeks)	Can you hear baby's heart?	Urine tests		Blood pressure	Mass (kg)
			Glucose	Protein		
27/10/04	9			NAD	125/70	
16 Nov	11+6			NAD	100/60	48.2
8/12/04	(14+4)	FMF	NAD	NAD	115/60	50kg
6.1.05	19 wks	FMF	NAD	NAD	110/60	52kg
1 Jan 05	19+5		NAD	NAD	130/70	55.3
2.2.05	23	H	NAN	NAN	115/60	54kg
Mar 05	27+	FMF	NIL			
3/3/05	284	FMF				
22.3			NAD			

Questions

1　What does an antenatal clinic do?

2　Give two tests a nurse might carry out on a pregnant woman.

3　How long does a baby need to stay inside its mother before it is ready to be born?

4　How much did the baby weigh when he was born?

5　When was the baby born?

Keywords

pregnant

antenatal

blood pressure

weight

height

2.3 Birth

How long does labour last?

*They said it would start during the night – and they were right! I had gone to bed and was trying to sleep when the first **contraction** came. It didn't really hurt but it was enough to keep me awake. I knew the contraction was the muscles tensing, getting ready to push the baby out. But I also knew that it was only the first sign of **labour** – a lot more had to happen.*

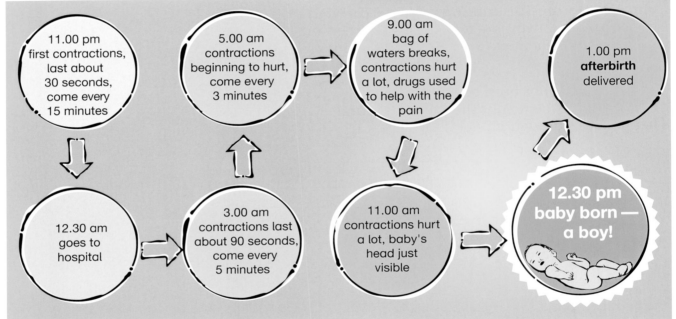

11.00 pm first contractions, last about 30 seconds, come every 15 minutes

5.00 am contractions beginning to hurt, come every 3 minutes

9.00 am bag of waters breaks, contractions hurt a lot, drugs used to help with the pain

1.00 pm **afterbirth** delivered

12.30 am goes to hospital

3.00 am contractions last about 90 seconds, come every 5 minutes

11.00 am contractions hurt a lot, baby's head just visible

12.30 pm baby born — a boy!

Questions

1 How long did it take from the start of labour to the baby being born?

2 How long after the start of labour did the mother need drugs for the pain?

3 What is a contraction?

4 What do contractions do?

5 List three things a woman may need to take into hospital when her labour begins.

6 Design a leaflet that explains what happens during labour. In your leaflet suggest things the partner could do to help reassure the mother.

Keywords

contraction

labour

afterbirth

Babies

2.4 Another mouth to feed

Can the earth cope?

Changing nappies, feeding, cleaning up sick... it's all such fun! And all the time the baby is growing and changing.

WEIGHT RECORD (birth to 2 yrs)

Date	Weight	Weight gain	Comments
9/2/05	3.82kg	birth weight	
20/2/05	4.50kg	0.68kg	
19/3/05	4.95kg	0.45kg	reflexes ok
16/4/05	5.12kg	0.17kg	small weight gain
14/5/05	5.54kg	0.42kg	
11/6/05	5.95kg		hearing, sight ok

Every second somewhere in the world a baby is born. Can the **planet** cope with this **population** increase?

People use up **resources** and produce waste. All human beings need: food and drink; somewhere to live; clothes to wear; a job to earn money. So every new baby is another burden for Planet Earth to carry. But some babies cost more than others. A person living in the USA uses 13 times as much of the world's resources as a person in Africa. Perhaps if we are going to survive we need to learn to share more fairly.

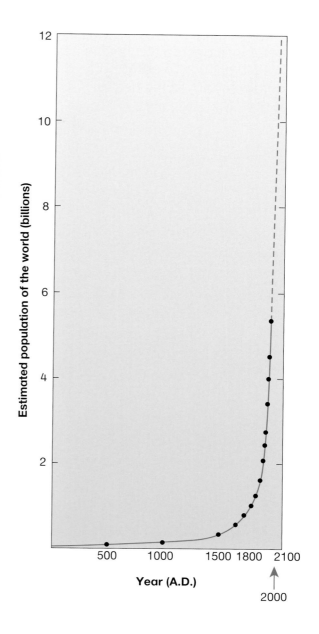

Questions

1 What is the baby's weight on May 14th?

2 What is the weight gain for 11th June?

3 Why did the health visitor make a note by the record for 16th April?

4 Use the information in the card above to plot a graph of the baby's weight gain from birth until May 14th.

5 If a baby is born every second, how many babies were born during a 50-minute Science Plus lesson?

6 Why is a population increase in a country in Africa less dangerous to the planet than the same increase in the USA or Europe?

Keywords

planet

population

resources

birth weight

reflex

hearing

sight

2 Data response: Looking after baby

Babies produce a lot of… liquid! Nappies absorb this until the child is old enough to use a potty. But which nappy is the best?

Water absorption by different disposable nappies

Nappy brand	Water absorbed by small size (suitable for baby less than 6 months)	Water absorbed by medium size (suitable for baby aged 6 to 12 months)	Water absorbed by large size (suitable for baby over 12 months old)
Swampers	15	24	37
Dumpers	11	20	29
Soggies	12	23	37

Data response

1 Which nappy absorbs the most liquid?

2 Which nappy absorbs the least liquid?

3 How much more water does the medium-sized Swampers nappy absorb than the medium-sized Dumpers?

4 Towelling nappies only come in one size. They absorb 35g of water. Give one advantage and one disadvantage of a towelling nappy for a 3-month-old baby.

5 If a newborn baby uses five nappies a day, how much would it cost to buy enough Swampers for one week?

6 A new brand, MegaZorb, absorbs more water so needs changing less often. A pack of 12 Megazorb nappies costs £3.95. The manufacturer claims only two MegaZorb nappies are needed for every three Dumpers nappies. A 6-month-old baby needs changing six times a day when using Dumpers. Would a week's supply of Megazorb nappies work out cheaper?

Research

7 Plan and carry out an investigation to find out which nappies absorb the most water. You will need to:
- Plan your investigation carefully.
- Decide how you will measure the water absorbed.
- Consider whether it is fair to compare nappies of different sizes.
- Interpret your results, looking for patterns in the results.

Babies

- Check that your results are reliable.
- Present your evidence, perhaps including a table of data or a chart in the presentation of your results.

Presentation

8 Doctors can now carry out lots of tests on an unborn baby to discover the baby's sex and show whether or not it is healthy. But are these tests a good thing? Different people have different opinions. What do you think?

Prepare a letter to a magazine for parents explaining your opinion on antenatal testing.

I want to know if the baby is sick in some way. I may want an abortion if the child is likely to be badly handicapped.

I don't want to know the sex of my baby. I just want it to be healthy.

These tests are not completely safe. I don't want one. And I don't know if I could have an abortion even if I knew the baby was handicapped in some way.

I heard of a baby that had a severe heart problem. He only lived for a few months and was in great pain. I think it would have been better if the parents had known about the heart defect before he was born and had an abortion.

Learning progress

I know:

- The testes make sperm and the ovaries make eggs. Fertilisation occurs when a sperm joins with an egg cell. Normally this fertilised egg divides to form a single baby. Identical twins occur when a fertilised egg divides into two before it starts to develop into a baby.

- The position of the penis, testis, sperm duct, ovary, oviduct, womb, vagina in a diagram.

- Periods stop during pregnancy and the woman gains weight. Periods start again soon after the baby is born.

- Medical staff measure the mother's blood pressure, height and weight during pregnancy to monitor the progress of the mother and foetus.

- The placenta and umbilical cord provide food and oxygen for the foetus and take away wastes. The bag of water protects the foetus from damage.

- The time before birth is called labour. It usually starts with contractions and the breaking of the waters. Labour can be painful. The placenta is delivered after the baby as the afterbirth.

- Data about the growth of the baby can be interpreted to provide information about the baby's development.

- The increase in human population is putting a strain on the Earth's environment.

- It is useful to collect and interpret data on human population growth.

I can:

- Show the position of the foetus, cord and placenta on a model.
- Read data from a graph.

3.1 Making fossils

Extinction

➡ How do fossils form?

Dinosaurs leave behind the biggest **fossils**. Sometimes they are bones or teeth. Sometimes they are piles of dinosaur **faeces** that have dried out and turned to stone! The faeces show scientists what the dinosaurs ate. Ever wondered what someone could work out from your faeces?

So how are fossils created in the first place?

| When a dinosaur died in a **swamp** its body rotted | ➡ | The dinosaur bones sank in the mud | ➡ | For millions of years, more and more sand and mud built up in layers over the bones | ➡ | Slowly the bones turned into stone fossils. Wind and rain wore away the rocks at the surface to expose the fossils. |

The real **Jurassic** Park was in Texas 200 million years ago. Many different types of dinosaur lived there. We know this because of the fossils found in the rocks. Not all of the dinosaurs were alive at the same time. The oldest rocks contain the oldest fossils. Usually, older rocks are underneath younger ones. We can tell the age of a rock, and the fossil it contains, by how deeply it is buried and the radioactive chemicals it contains.

Questions

1 List the main things that must happen for a fossil to be formed.
2 Draw a cliff showing five layers of rock.
3 On your cliff diagram, label the oldest layer.
4 On your cliff diagram, label the layer that will have the youngest fossils.
5 Give two ways to decide the age of a rock.
6 Which parts of a dinosaur are most likely to become fossils? Why?

Keywords

dinosaur

fossil

faeces

swamp

Jurassic

3.2 Dino adaptations

What were dinosaurs like?

A modern meat-eater has sharp teeth and large jaws. If we find a dinosaur jaw bone with many sharp teeth we can assume that it came from a meat-eater. Large claws also suggest that the dinosaur was a meat-eater. These differences are called **adaptations**. The area where they live is called their **habitat**.

Tyrannosaurus Rex was a hunter with powerful muscles and sharp teeth and claws. **Ichthyosaurus** was a dinosaur that swam like a fish. It had a smooth body to move through the water easily. The **Apatosaurus** had a huge body and a long neck to reach the leaves in the tallest trees. These various types of dinosaur are called different **species**.

Even dinosaurs of the same type would be slightly different. One T. Rex might be taller, or stronger than the others in that area. He might be a better hunter and get more food. He might breed to produce stronger, taller dinosaurs. Over millions of years these changes might lead to a completely new species.

Questions

1 List the adaptations the Ichthyosaurus had for life in water.
2 List the adaptations the Apatosaurus had for life on land.
3 List the adaptations that the T. Rex had for life as a hunter.
4 How do you think a longer neck would help an Apatosaurus survive?
5 How do you think being able to run faster would help a T. Rex survive?
6 List the adaptations of a tiger to its diet. How many of these adaptations has T. Rex got?

Keywords

adaptation

habitat

Tyrannosaurus Rex

Ichthyosaurus

species

Apatosaurus

3.3 Where did we come from?

How old is the Earth?

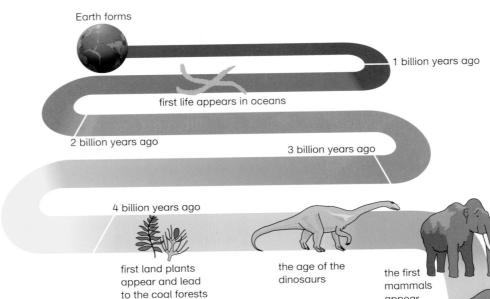

Earth forms

1 billion years ago

first life appears in oceans

2 billion years ago

3 billion years ago

4 billion years ago

first land plants appear and lead to the coal forests

the age of the dinosaurs

the first mammals appear

first apes appear

first humans appear

Today

The Earth is about 7000 million years old. Life probably began about 3500 million years ago as very simple cells. Over time new species developed and old ones became **extinct**. Many changes over millions of years led to the living things we see today. This idea is called **evolution** and most scientists think it explains how human beings developed.

Scientists use information from **fossils**, the shape of the land and even some of the chemicals inside our cells to build a picture of the Earth's past. We have to **interpret** the clues left behind.

But scientists do not always agree. This is not a bad thing – it keeps scientists thinking and looking for new information. Eventually we hope to agree as more **evidence** becomes available.

Fossils are rare but there is so much other evidence and we have not found a better way to explain where we came from. I believe in the theory of evolution.

Fossils are very rare and difficult to interpret. It is easy to believe we have made many mistakes and I do not believe in the theory of evolution.

Questions

1 Make up your own sentence using the word 'extinct'.
2 When did the planet Earth probably form?
3 When did life begin on planet Earth?
4 What were the earliest life forms like?
5 When did the dinosaurs become extinct?

6 Scientists do not always agree. Give two reasons why they might disagree.

Keywords

extinct

evolution

fossils

interpret

evidence

3.4 Wanted! (Or not?)

> **Why did some animals become extinct?**

Giant Panda

Habitat: lower mountain slopes of Northern China

Threats: habitat destruction to create farms, houses

Outlook: looking hopeful – a good conservation programme now protects 45% of the panda's natural habitat

Numbers: 600 in the wild

EASTERN LOWLAND GORILLA

Habitat: rainforests of the Democratic Republic of the Congo, Africa

Threats: habitat destruction by illegal mining, hunting for meat

Outlook: worrying, recent surveys show a big fall in the population

Numbers: perhaps 30,000

DODO

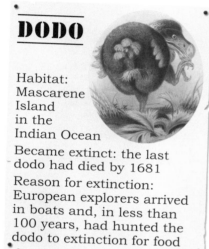

Habitat: Mascarene Island in the Indian Ocean

Became extinct: the last dodo had died by 1681

Reason for extinction: European explorers arrived in boats and, in less than 100 years, had hunted the dodo to extinction for food

Dinosaurs

Habitat: All over the world

Became extinct: about 200 million years ago

Reason for extinction: no-one is certain

Sabre-toothed tiger

Habitat: North American grasslands

Became extinct: 10,000 years ago

Reason for extinction: uncertain, but it may have been climate change in the Ice Age when the world became much colder

Nowadays human beings are probably the biggest threat to animals and plants. We are **changing** their **environment** and they may not be able to survive. Animals that are **adapted** to life in the jungle die as the rainforest is cleared. Animals adapted to cold are dying as the Earth gets hotter by global warming. And deserts are growing so plants and animals that cannot survive drought are dying out.

Questions

1 Which endangered animal lives in China?

2 When did the sabre-toothed tiger die out?

3 What may have caused the dinosaurs to die out?

4 Why can any change lead to problems for some animals and plants?

5 Give three things that human beings are doing to make the world more dangerous for animals and plants.

6 Write a letter to the President of the Democratic Republic of Congo explaining why they should protect the lowland gorillas.

Keywords

change

environment

adapted

3 Data response: Wailing about whales?

Blue whale

Weight:	180,000 kg
Length:	25 m
Feed on:	krill and plankton
Top speed:	45 kmph
Life span:	35 years
Species status:	endangered and protected

Sperm whale

Weight:	46,000 kg
Length:	17.5 m
Feed on:	giant squid, octopus, fish, eels
Top speed:	40 kmph
Life span:	75 years
Species status:	endangered

Killer whale

Weight:	4800 kg
Length:	8 m
Feed on:	fish, squid, dolphins
Top speed:	48 kmph
Life span:	60 years
Species status:	abundant

Mini ONE

Weight:	1200 kg
Length:	2.5 m
Feed on:	petrol
Top speed:	200 kmph
Life span:	10 years
Species status:	abundant

Data response

1 Which whale species weighs 46,000 kg?

2 A mystery whale weighs over 100,000 kg. What species is it?

3 What is the shortest whale?

4 How many Mini ONEs weigh the same as a single killer whale?

5 Draw a bar chart to show the top speed of the three whale species listed here and a Mini ONE.

6 Which is the only whale species that is not endangered?

Research

7 Do an internet search on the dangers to whale species. They have been hunted for many years and their numbers have fallen. Nowadays global warming may be changing the temperature of the oceans and altering the whales' environment. Large ships seem to be confusing the whales and some are even damaged by collisions with oil tankers.

Presentation

8 Prepare a presentation about the dangers facing whale species all over the world. Suggest how they might be protected for future generations.

Learning progress

I know:

- Fossils tell us about living organisms from long ago. They form from the hard parts of dead bodies and are buried in rocks of the same age.

- Life on Earth began about 3500 million years ago with very simple living things. These have been changing ever since due to evolution.

- 'Variations' are the differences between living things of the same type. Living things compete for shelter, food and mates, in order to survive. The best-adapted survivors breed and pass on their features to the next generation.

- A species is a type of living organism. A habitat is the environment where a species lives. If this habitat changes dramatically the species may become extinct. Better adapted species may replace it.

- Human beings can cause extinction of some species by changing their habitats (gorillas, orang-utans, pandas), hunting them (dodo) or pollution. Dinosaurs, sabre-toothed tigers and dodos are extinct animals.

- Scientists do not always agree about an explanation. They discuss their differences. This goes on until people are convinced by the evidence.

- A variety of options are available to protect living things that are near extinction.

I can:

- Collect (scientific) information about an endangered or extinct species.

- Place things onto a timeline when given information about when they lived.

4.1 Save a life!

➪ **How can I save a life?**

These people are trained professionals working in dangerous conditions. You can save a life – if you know what to do!

A person cannot live without **oxygen** for more than three minutes. The blood carries oxygen from the lungs to other parts of the body. If a person loses a lot of blood, stops breathing or the heart stops beating, then the oxygen cannot get to the parts of the body that need it. That person could die.

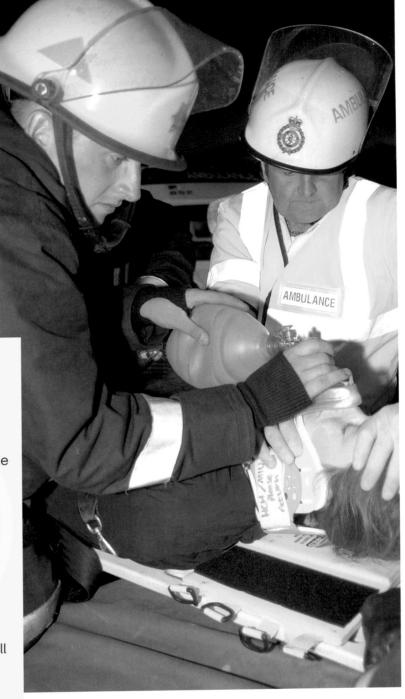

➕ 1 **Assess** the situation
   Find out what happened and who is injured.

➕ 2 Make safe
   Make sure that the person is no longer in danger and that no-one else is going to get hurt.

➕ 3 Give emergency first aid – use the ABC code

   (a) **Airways** – are they open? Remove a blockage if necessary.

   (b) **Breathing** – is the casualty breathing? Give the kiss of life if necessary.

   (c) **Circulation** – is the heart still beating? If yes, check for signs of **bleeding**. Stop the flow of blood.

Casualty

Questions

1 Why is it important that the casualty keeps breathing?
2 Why is it important that the heart keeps beating?
3 Write out the three stages of emergency aid.
4 Why is it important to make sure the area is safe?
5 List the information you would need to give if you dialled 999.
6 For what does the body use oxygen?

Keywords

oxygen
assess
airways
breathing
circulation
bleeding

4.2 Have a heart!

How does the heart work?

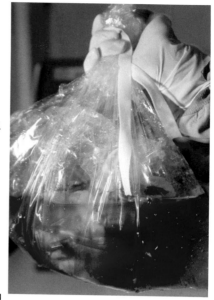

Until a very short time ago this heart was beating inside someone. But he died in a car accident. He carried a donor card which said that he wanted to help someone after his death. His heart will soon be beating in another person's chest. This person's own heart has been damaged. Without this transplant he will die.

The heart is really two **pumps** stuck together. The left side pumps blood from the body to the **lungs**. The right side takes blood from the lungs and pumps it to the body. In the lungs the blood loses **carbon dioxide** and gains **oxygen**. We breathe out the carbon dioxide. The blood carries the oxygen to other parts of the body.

The blood leaves the heart in tubes called **arteries**. The arteries divide into smaller and smaller tubes. The smallest tubes are called **capillaries**. These are so small you cannot see them without a microscope. The capillaries link up into larger and larger tubes to take blood back to the heart. These tubes are called **veins**.

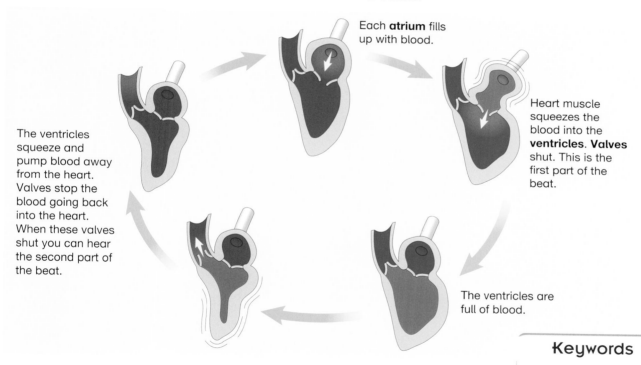

Each **atrium** fills up with blood.

Heart muscle squeezes the blood into the **ventricles**. **Valves** shut. This is the first part of the beat.

The ventricles are full of blood.

The ventricles squeeze and pump blood away from the heart. Valves stop the blood going back into the heart. When these valves shut you can hear the second part of the beat.

Questions

1 List the blood vessels carrying blood away from the heart.

2 List the blood vessels carrying blood towards the heart.

3 Imagine you are a blood cell in the left atrium of the heart. List the parts of the heart you go through before you leave along the aorta.

4 What happens to the blood in the lungs?

5 What do the valves do in the heart?

Keywords

pump
lungs
carbon dioxide
oxygen
artery
capillary
vein
atrium
ventricles
valves

4.3 You've got to move it! Move it!

> **What happens to the heart when we exercise?**

The heart is a **muscle** and it gets stronger with **exercise**. This cross-country cyclist is giving his heart a good work out! Riding up and down hills and carrying his bike across streams and rivers needs lots of energy. The heart beats more quickly to make sure the muscles get enough **blood** containing food and **oxygen** to make this energy.

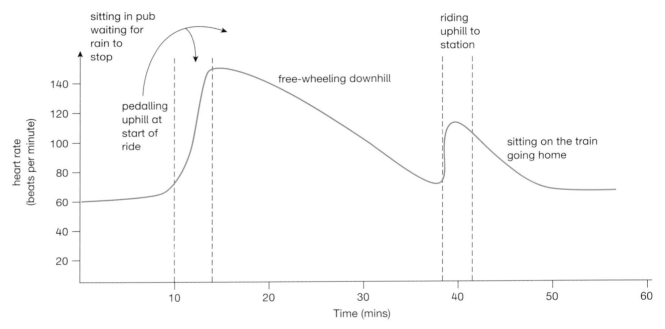

Questions

1 What is the heart made of?

2 Why does the **heart rate** rise during exercise?

3 Rank the following in order, starting with the lowest heart rate and finishing with the highest: running, watching television, sleeping, walking to school.

4 What is the highest heart rate in the graph?

5 What is the difference between the highest and lowest heart rates in the graph?

Keywords

muscle

exercise

blood

oxygen

heart rate

4.4 Keep healthy

 How can I keep my heart healthy?

These people are storing up trouble for themselves (and we don't just mean the hair!). A little **exercise**, less food and giving up smoking would add years to their lives. It would also make them feel more energetic. **Arteries** carry blood at high pressure and have thicker walls than **veins**. At the moment they are blocking their arteries and veins with fat and forcing their hearts to work too hard just to pump blood around their bodies.

Smoking damages the lungs. Chemicals in cigarette smoke also make the heart beat more quickly all the time.

People who are **overweight** put a strain on their heart. The blood has to travel further around their body than in thinner people.

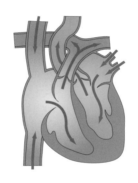

As we get older our hearts begin to weaken.

Lack of exercise means muscles go flabby. since the heart is a muscle it can get weaker if it becomes unfit. Exercise encourages the heart to grow and develop.

Sometimes a fatty substance coats the inside walls of **blood vessels**. This makes the blood vessel narrower. The heart has to work much harder to pump blood along it.

Questions

1 List the things that can damage your heart.

2 Sort your list into things we can prevent and things we cannot do anything about.

3 Describe three ways to prevent your heart being damaged.

4 Exercise makes your heart beat faster. Plan an investigation to find out how different sorts of exercise affect your heart rate.

5 Design a poster for a local sports centre, telling people how to look after their hearts. Think about all the different people who will see the poster: old and young, male and female.

Keywords

exercise

artery

vein

smoking

overweight

blood vessels

4 Data response: Keeping healthy

Cause of death among 10 000 British doctors who started smoking in 1950

Killed by	Never smoked	Smokes 1–14 a day	Smokes 15–24 a day	Smokes more than 24 a day
Heart attack	572	802	892	1025
High blood pressure	32	28	51	60
Stroke	152	167	231	235
Asthma	4	6	8	6

Never smoked regularly

80%

50%

33%

Current cigarette smokers:
— 1–14/day
— ≥25/day

8%

% Alive

Age

£5 for a pack of 20

Smoking habits of British doctors

Year	Smoker	Non-smoker
1951	62%	48%
1991	18%	82%

Data response

1 How many doctors killed by heart attacks were non-smokers?

2 How many doctors killed by heart attacks smoked fewer than 15 cigarettes a day?

3 If you smoke more than 24 cigarettes a day you are twice as likely to die of a heart attack compared with a non-smoker. Do the figures in Table 1 support this statement?

4 Draw a bar chart to show the change in death rates due to strokes compared with the number of cigarettes smoked per day.

5 What percentage of doctors smoked in 1951?

6 What percentage of doctors smoked in 1991?

7 Why do you think these numbers changed so much?

8 Use data from the life expectancy graphs to mark each of these statements 'true' or 'false':
   A 80% of people who do not smoke live to the age of 80.
   B 50% of people who smoke more than 25 cigarettes a day are dead by the age of 70.
   C The more you smoke the younger you will be when you die.
   D Even smoking less than 14 cigarettes a day increases your chance of dying early.

Casualty

9 'My uncle smoked 100 cigarettes for 40 years and was eventually run over by a bus. He shows that smoking is safe!' What could you say to this person about the need for more evidence?

10 A man smokes 20 cigarettes a day. How much will this cost in a year?

11 A woman spends £2000 on cigarettes! If she smokes 15 every day how long will her cigarettes last?

Research

11 Use a smoking machine to look at the effect of cigarette smoke on yeast growth.

12 Plan and carry out an investigation to test one of the following ideas:
- The first third of the cigarette is less dangerous than the last third.
- Low tar cigarettes are almost as dangerous as high tar cigarettes.
- Filters on cigarettes make them safer.

Presentation

13 Work with a friend to develop a 5-minute radio programme in which two experts discuss smoking. One wants to ban smoking everywhere because of the health risks. The other believes this is impossible because smokers will simply break the law. At the end of the discussion they should agree on a joint way forward.

Learning progress

I know:

- In an emergency I have to check for airways, breathing and circulation (the ABC code) and give first aid if necessary.

- The heart pumps blood around the body. It is made of muscle and needs a good blood supply to give it food and oxygen to do this job.

- Arteries have thick walls and carry blood away from the heart. Veins have thin walls and carry blood back to the heart. Capillaries are very small and carry blood from arteries to veins.

- During exercise the muscles need more blood so the heart beats faster. The heart rate slows down again after exercise. This happens more quickly in fit people compared with unfit people.

- Fatty foods, smoking and lack of exercise can lead to problems with the blood vessels and heart. Some people have a greater risk of heart attacks than others. This depends on lifestyle and genetics. To improve the health of your heart you should eat a healthy diet, avoid smoking and take regular exercise.

I can:

- Measure a person's pulse rate.
- Devise a 10-minute-a-day fitness programme.

Building bodies

5

5.1 Beautiful bodies?

Which chemicals do our bodies contain?

People look so different – but we're all the same underneath! In fact 70% of our bodies is just water! The solids in our bodies are made of proteins, fats and carbohydrates. We also contain small amounts of vitamins and minerals. We get all of these things from the food that we eat. What are they used for?

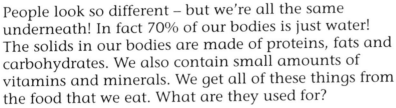

Food type	Used to:
Proteins	make muscles and skin
Fats	make brains and skin and give us energy
Carbohydrates	give us **energy** to stay alive
Minerals	build teeth and bones
Vitamins	keep us healthy

Questions

1 What kind of person do you think will need the most protein?

2 What kind of person will need the least energy-giving foods?

3 What is protein used to build?

4 A man weighs roughly 150 kg. What is the weight of water in his body?

5 Why do teenagers tend to need more protein in their diets than pensioners?

6 What effects will a lack of protein have on the body?

Keywords

protein

fat

carbohydrate

energy

mineral

vitamin

5.2 Special bodies

 Why do we need different bodies?

We are what we eat. We use our food to build us up and give us **energy**. The food we eat is called our **diet**. Scientists sort the food we eat into groups so that they can work out if we are getting a healthy diet. If there is something wrong with our diet there will be something wrong with our body. Of course, different people need different diets!

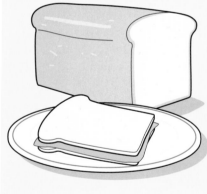

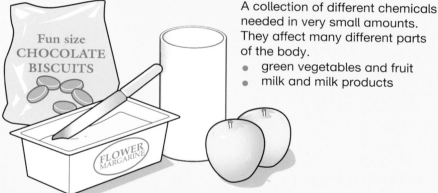

Carbohydrates
Give the body energy
- sugars
- bread
- vegetables

Vitamins and minerals
A collection of different chemicals needed in very small amounts. They affect many different parts of the body.
- green vegetables and fruit
- milk and milk products

Proteins
Build muscles
- lean meat
- beans

Fats
Store energy in the body
- butter and margarine
- chocolate
- fatty meat

Questions

1 List the foods you think a Sumo wrestler would eat.
2 List the foods you think a ballet dancer would eat.
3 List the foods you ate yesterday.
4 Sort your food into carbohydrates, fats and proteins.
5 Are you getting a good balance of the different food types?
6 Why doesn't everyone have the same diet?

Keywords

energy

diet

carbohydrates

vitamins

minerals

proteins

fats

5.3 Label lore

 What foods are good for bodybuilders?

To get a body like this you need to watch what you eat and make sure you get plenty of **protein** – and not much **fat**!

Most foods are a **mixture**. Chicken has lots of protein and little fat. Beef has lots of protein but more fat. Bodybuilders need the protein but not the fat. They eat lots of grilled chicken and even buy special foods for bodybuilders. Many take vitamin and mineral pills because they do not always eat enough fruit and vegetables.

Many dieters only look for the **energy** content of the food on the label. They avoid foods with lots of energy. This means they use up their stored fat and lose weight. But they need to get enough of the food groups like proteins and vitamins and minerals or they can become ill. In some parts of the world poor people do not get enough protein. They suffer from an illness called kwashikior. It does not usually kill them but makes them very weak and unhealthy.

4 STEWING STEAKS

Typical values per 100g (3.5oz)
ENERGY   223kcal, 932kJ
PROTEIN   13.9g
CARBOHYDRATE   0.0g
FATS   11.0g

Skinless Frozen Chicken
Typical values per 100g (3.5oz)
ENERGY   210kcal, 880kJ
PROTEIN   33.2g
CARBOHYDRATE 0.0g
FATS   5.4g

Chocolate Biscuit (KitKat)
Typical values per 100g
ENERGY 503kcal, 2103kJ
PROTEIN 7.6g
CARBOHYDRATE 59.1g
FATS 26.2g

INGREDIEN
HYDROGE
WHEY PO
FLAVOUI
ETABLE
THIS P

Roasted Salted Peanuts
Typical values per 100g
ENERGY 600kcal, 2489kJ
PROTEIN 29.0g
CARBOHYDRATE 8.6g
FATS 50.0g

Questions

1 Almost all foods are mixtures of different food types. Explain what the word 'mixture' means.
2 Is it a good idea to eat a **diet** with only one type of food? Explain your answer.
3 Sort the foods above so that the one with the most protein comes first.
4 Which foods would a bodybuilder try not to eat? Why?
5 Why do bodybuilders eat a high protein diet?
6 Draw a bar chart to show the carbohydrate, fat and protein in chicken. You could draw another one for beef.

Keywords

protein
fat
mixture
energy
diet

Building bodies

5.4 That takes guts!

  How does your gut work?

Food must be **digested** before it is **absorbed**. Digestion means to break the food down into small particles. Digesting food takes guts! **Gut** is the scientific name for the tube that takes food from our mouth to the **anus**. As the food travels along the tube it is broken down and absorbed by the body.

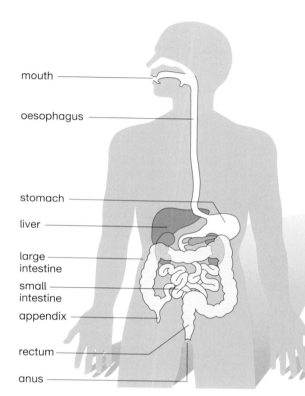

mouth

oesophagus

stomach

liver

large intestine

small intestine

appendix

rectum

anus

The mouth breaks food into smaller lumps. **Saliva** helps to break down starchy foods to sugar

Acid and enzymes in the **stomach** break down the **protein**. The acid kills any bacteria in the food. Here the food is a watery sludge.

The **small intestine** breaks down foods. It can also absorb food into the blood.

The **large intestine** absorbs water from the food. The food becomes more solid.

The **rectum** stores the remaining waste food. The ring of muscle in the anus holds the waste in the body until you go to the toilet.

Questions

1 List the parts of the gut that food passes through from mouth to anus.

2 Draw an outline of the gut. Colour in red the parts that break food down.

3 Colour in blue the parts of the gut that absorb food.

4 Draw a flow chart to show what happens to food in the gut. Start in the mouth and finish when the food passes out of the body.

5 Where does protein digestion begin in the gut?

6 Where is most of the water absorbed in the gut?

Keywords

digest

absorb

gut

anus

saliva

acid

stomach

protein

small intestine

large intestine

rectum

5 Data response: It's all just junk!

We all know we should eat healthy food – but unhealthy food tastes so good!
Which would you rather have for lunch?

Nutritional value of different foods

Food	Protein (g)	Fat (g)	Sugar (g)	Energy/ calories
Cheese salad sandwich made with brown bread	22.7	30.3	12.9	547
Boiled egg	6.3	5	0	75
Yoghurt	4.5	4.2	6.6	82
Bottle of water	0	0	0	0
Bar of chocolate	5	18	18	280
Bottle of fizzy drink	0	0	50.5	210
One apple	0.3	0.5	21	81
Chocolate teacake	1.2	4	13.4	97
Packet of crisps	1.6	8.3	0.5	131
Marshmallow-type sweets	1.6	0	32.5	165

Calories used in 30 minutes

Activity	Calories
Aerobics	185
Weightlifting	150
Mountain biking	280
Soccer	250
Housework	100
Washing the car	100
Sitting in class	60
Sleeping	30
Weeding the garden	150
Walking	160

Data response

1 How much sugar is there in a single chocolate bar?

2 How much fat is there in two packets of crisps?

3 Which snack gives you the most protein?

4 Which snack has the lowest calorie count?

5 Work out the total protein content in the healthy lunchbox.

6 Work out the total sugar content in the unhealthy lunchbox.

7 How long would you have to walk to use up the calories in a chocolate bar?

8 Make a collection of food labels and sort them into groups. The groups should be based on your ideas of what are healthy foods. Include at least 20 foods.

Woah!: these are foods that you'd be better off without or eating in small amounts every now and then.

OK!: these are good foods – but not too often!

Go for it!: you can eat plenty of these every day – and they'll do you good!

Presentation

9 Is junk food bad for you? Prepare two adverts for a teenage magazine. They should both point out the healthy things about the two lunchboxes on page 32. Each advert should be up to 200 words long, include at least two pictures and be scientifically correct.

Learning progress

I know:

● Different people have different lifestyles and need different diets. Body builders, athletes and teenagers need lots of protein and energy foods. Dieters and people with inactive lifestyles need less. In some parts of the world, people do not have enough protein or energy in their diets.

● The body is mainly water, with carbohydrates, protein, fats, vitamins and minerals. These come from our food and drink.

● Meat, fish and eggs are good supplies of protein. Milk, butter and chocolate contain a lot of fat. Bread, potatoes and sugar contain lots of carbohydrate.

● On food packaging there is information about the nutritional values of the food.

● Tests can be carried out to determine the levels of starch, sugar, protein and fats within food.

● Food must be digested before it is absorbed into the body. Enzymes carry out this digestion and each type of food (starch, proteins, fats) need a particular type of enzyme.

● Absorption of food happens mainly in the intestine. Water is absorbed in the large intestine.

● The position of the mouth, stomach, small and large intestines, rectum and anus in a diagram of the human gut.

I can:

● Plan my daily protein intake.

● Safely carry out a food test for starch.

Respond • Research • Present

6.1 Keeping control

 Why is overheating dangerous?

Explorers cope with extreme cold and heat just to go somewhere that no-one has been before. The skier is having fun in temperatures well below freezing. The quad biker is driving through a desert where the temperature often rises above 40°C! Hot enough to fry an egg by cracking it on a flat stone!

But inside your body the **temperature** stays at about 37°C. Our cells are damaged if it changes by more than a few degrees. It's the same for the amount of water and sugar in our **blood**. The body works hard to keep these constant even if the outside environment changes. Our cells live in an **internal environment** created by the body.

Temperature	Body condition	
45	You are dead.	
40	You pass out. You are in a very dangerous condition now.	
39	You feel very hot. You start to talk nonsense and maybe see and hear things that are not there. You will probably be sick.	
38	You feel hot and start to **sweat**. You may well be a bit irritable.	
37	Normal temperature. You feel warm and comfortable.	

Questions

1 What does the phrase 'internal environment' mean?

2 What is the normal body temperature for human beings?

3 At what temperature will you pass out?

4 List three ways in which the body tries to lower your body temperature.

5 List three things the body tries to keep within narrow limits in the internal environment.

6 Plan an investigation to see how exercise affects your body temperature.

Keywords

temperature

blood

internal environment

sweat

Control systems

6.2 Cold enough to freeze ...

⟹ **Why does hypothermia kill?**

He's well wrapped up against the cold. He doesn't look very cheerful though. Perhaps he's wearing shorts!

Your body works best at 37°C. If you get too cold you could get **hypothermia**. This means that you start to feel sleepy and can pass into a very deep sleep called a **coma**. You could die.

Hot

Blood flows to the skin's surface so it cools down in the air. You look redder.

Sweat is released. It takes heat from you when it evaporates.

Hairs lie flat so less air is trapped.

Cold

The blood flow to the ears and nose is reduced to cut down heat loss.

Muscles shiver to create heat.

Most blood keeps away from the skin to reduce heat loss. You look paler.

Hair stands on end to trap warm air.

Temperature	Body condition	
37	Normal **temperature**. You feel warm and comfortable.	🙂
36	You feel cold and start to **shiver**.	😐
35	Shivering stops – but you start to become very confused and sleepy.	🙁
25	You are now in a coma. Your breathing and pulse are very low. Heart attacks can occur.	☹️
20	You are dead.	😵

Questions

1. What is hypothermia?
2. List the things your body does to keep you warm in cold weather.
3. At what temperature do you pass out?
4. Which body part loses the most heat?
5. How do clothes help to keep you warm?
6. Why is a walker with a shaved head more likely to suffer from hypothermia than one with thick long **hair**?

Keywords

hypothermia

coma

temperature

shiver

hair

6.3 Controlling water levels

How does your body control its water levels?

We can only live for a few days without having a drink. 70% of our body is **water**. Water is needed to make blood and digestive juices. The chemical reactions in our cells only work properly if there is enough water around. The **kidneys** control the amount of water in our body.

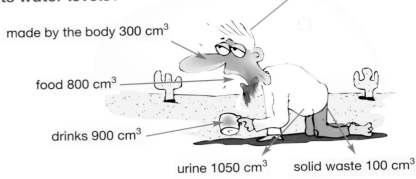

evaporation 850 cm³

made by the body 300 cm³

food 800 cm³

drinks 900 cm³

urine 1050 cm³   solid waste 100 cm³

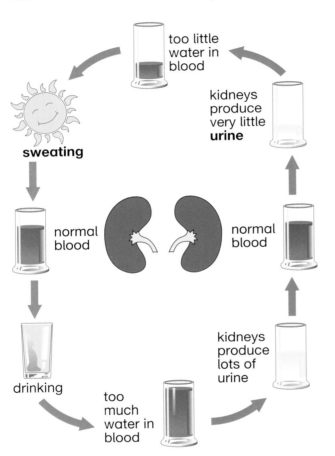

Water level	Body condition	
100	Healthy and happy.	
99	You are already feeling **thirsty**.	
96	You are moody, tired and irritable.	
94	You look pale and ill. You stop sweating to save water.	
80	You are dead.	

Questions

1 Why is it important for people to drink water?

2 Which part of your body gets rid of extra water?

3 What else do kidneys remove from your body?

4 Why do you produce less **urine** on days when you do not have much to drink?

5 Work out how much water we take in each day and how much water we lose in a day.

6 An expedition is taking enough water for six people for a week. How much do they need to take?

Keywords

water

kidney

sweat

urine

thirsty

6.4 Keeping sweet!

How does your body control sugar levels?

Sir Steve Redgrave has **diabetes** but it didn't stop him winning four Olympic gold medals! He does need to be careful about what he eats and he needs injections every day to control the level of glucose in his blood.

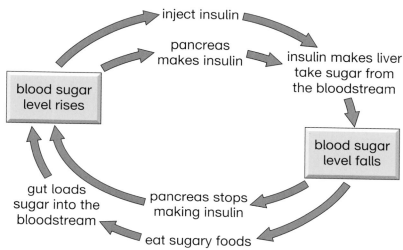

A lot of the food we eat contains **sugar**. We use some sugar for energy straight away and store the rest for later. A chemical called **insulin** tells your body when there is spare sugar to **store**. People who do not make insulin have an illness called diabetes. They do not store extra sugar. Too much sugar stays in their blood. This causes high blood pressure and passes out in their urine. Diabetic people need to **inject** themselves with insulin every day.

If a diabetic person's blood sugar level falls too low they may feel faint, become unconscious or even go into a **coma**. If you find a diabetic in a coma try to wake them up and give them a spoonful of honey or a sweet drink.

Questions

1 What do we need sugar for?
2 List three foods which contain a lot of sugar.
3 What is diabetes?
4 How can diabetes be treated?
5 What could happen to a diabetic person who does not have his or her injections?
6 What should you do to help a diabetic person in a coma?

Keywords

diabetes

sugar

insulin

store

inject

coma

6 Data response: Extreme environments

Emergency Procedure for Mountain Accident

DO get inside a tent or survival bag if possible.

DO avoid areas where the wind is strong.

DO report your location as clearly as possible to mountain rescue.

DO stay together.

DO NOT move around. Wait for rescue.

DO remove wet clothing – if you can replace it with dry clothes.

DO wear a hat.

DO NOT go to sleep.

Fabrics available for snow jacket manufacture

Fabric	Is it waterproof?	Is it windproof?	Is it a good insulator?	Does it split easily?	Cost?	Weight	What is it made from?
Icetech 7	★	★★	★★★	★★	★★	★	Wool and plastic
Icetech 15	★	★★	★★★★	★★	★★★	★★	Wool and plastic
Icetech 22	★	★★★	★★★★★	★★	★★★	★★★	Wool and plastic
Hydrofabric	★★★★★	★★★★★	★	★★★★	★	★	Plastic
Envirofleece 11	★	★★	★★★	★	★★★	★	Recycled plastic
Envirofleece 35	★	★★★	★★★★★	★	★★★★	★★	Recycled plastic
MoreTex™	★★★★★	★★★★★	★	★★★★	★★★	★	Plastic
Nuskin 2	★★★★	★★★★★	★★	★	★	★	Plastic
CottonFlex	★★	★★★	★★	★★★	★	★★	Cotton

The more stars the better, so Hydrofabric resists tearing better than Icetech 7.

Data response

1 Which fabric is the best insulator?

2 Which fabric splits most easily?

3 Which is the heaviest fabric?

4 Give one disadvantage of a jacket made from Hydrofabric only.

5 Many jackets have an inner layer for warmth and an outer layer for waterproofing. Choose a fabric for each of these layers. Give reasons for your choices.

Control systems

Look at the advice from mountain rescue.

6 Why should you wear a hat?

7 Why not go to sleep if you are tired?

8 Why not split up to look for rescuers?

Research

9 Plan an investigation to find out which of three hats is the best at keeping your head warm.

Presentation

10 Every year people die in the UK from cold. These people are usually pensioners living in draughty, badly-insulated homes. They worry about paying their electricity and gas bills so do not turn the heating up high enough. Prepare a leaflet to explain why staying warm is so important.

Learning progress

I know:

- Changes in our surroundings can affect our body's internal environment. The body tries to control this change in the internal environment.

- The body's normal temperature is 37°C. Shivering, exercise and some illnesses increase this temperature. A dangerously high body temperature is called a fever. Sweating and moving blood towards the skin lowers this temperature.

- A dangerously low body temperature is called hypothermia. Body fat, raising hair on the skin and drawing blood away from the skin helps to reduce loss of heat from the body.

- The body needs water to survive and gets this from food and drink. Water leaves the body in sweat, air breathed out from the lungs and in urine. The kidneys produce urine with lots of water when we have plenty and very concentrated urine when we have to save water.

- The sugar level in the blood must be kept within limits. Food makes the level rise and exercise makes it fall. The body uses a hormone called insulin to control the blood sugar level. Diabetics cannot control their blood sugar level and some need to have insulin injections and follow special diets.

- The position of the kidney and bladder on a diagram.

I can:

- Produce a poster to warn old people about the risks of hypothermia.

- Use a thermometer to measure temperature.

Gasping for breath

7.1 A vital gas

 Why do we need oxygen?

In a fire most people are killed by the fumes and lack of oxygen. That's why firefighters wear breathing apparatus in burning buildings. The cylinders contain compressed air. Inside the fire engines they have cylinders of **oxygen** ready for **casualties** whose lungs have been damaged by smoke.

But why do we need oxygen? Every cell in your body needs **energy**. The **glucose** from food reacts with the oxygen to provide energy. This process is called **respiration**.

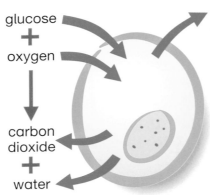

glucose
+
oxygen

↓

carbon dioxide
+
water

energy for:
- growing
- repairing any damage
- dividing to make more cells
- everything the cell does

The water and **carbon dioxide** are waste products. You get rid of them when you breathe out. On a cold day you can see the moisture in your breath. You cannot see the carbon dioxide because it is a colourless gas. You can detect it with limewater. Carbon dioxide makes **limewater** turn milky white.

Questions

1 What kills most people in fires?
2 Why do firefighters carry oxygen in their fire engines?
3 Where does the glucose in the cells of the body come from?
4 What is produced when glucose reacts with oxygen?
5 How can you detect carbon dioxide gas?

Keywords

oxygen
casualty
energy
glucose
respiration
carbon dioxide
limewater

7.2 Nice pairs of lungs

 How do we breathe in and out?

You need a good set of lungs for this! Actually, it's the muscles attached to your ribs that allow you to breathe in and out.

Not everyone's lungs can hold the same amount of air. The volume of air you can hold in your lungs is called your **lung capacity**. An average man may have a capacity of 5–6 litres. A fit athlete may hold 7 litres. A small child would have a smaller lung capacity.

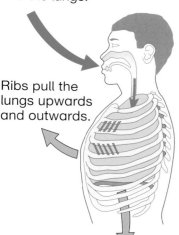

Air is sucked into the lungs.

Ribs pull the lungs upwards and outwards.

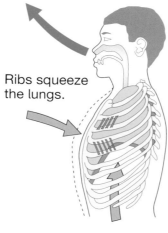

Air is squeezed out of the lungs.

Ribs squeeze the lungs.

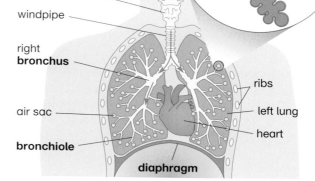

voice box
windpipe
right **bronchus**
air sac
bronchiole
diaphragm
ribs
left lung
heart

Air sac
Oxygen goes from the air into the bloodstream. Carbon dioxide goes the other way.

Questions

1 In which direction do the ribs move when someone breathes out?

2 What is the name of the tube that carries air from your mouth to your lungs?

3 What happens to the air when it reaches the air sacs?

4 Draw a flow chart to show how air gets from the mouth to the air sacs in the lungs.

5 Plan an investigation to find out if athletes do have bigger lungs than unfit people of the same height.

Keywords

lung capacity
bronchus
bronchiole
air sac
diaphragm

7.3 Fighting for breath

What is asthma?

This boy has **asthma**. Asthma is a condition that causes the **airways** to narrow. This stops a person breathing in and out properly. The **symptoms** that people with asthma have are coughing, wheezing and being short of breath.

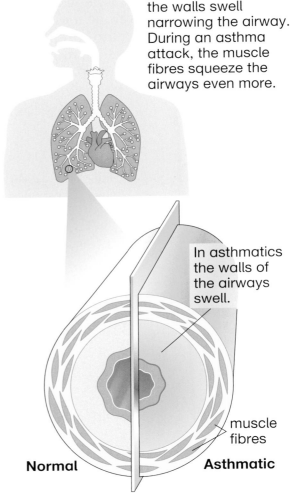

In an asthmatic person the walls swell narrowing the airway. During an asthma attack, the muscle fibres squeeze the airways even more.

In asthmatics the walls of the airways swell.

muscle fibres

Normal   **Asthmatic**

Asthma reduces:

- the speed that people can breathe in and out, and
- the lung capacity.

This is because the walls of the airways are swollen so the space for air is smaller. The airways narrow further if the person exercises or if the air is polluted.

People with asthma may need to use an **inhaler** like the one in the picture. There are two types of inhaler – **relievers** or **preventers**. The doctor may also prescribe drugs that are **protectors**. They help to prevent another attack.

Type of inhaler	What does it do?
Reliever	Relieves the symptoms. Makes breathing easier.
Preventer	Reduces the inflammation in the airways. Helps to prevent an attack.

Questions

1 Describe what happens to the airways of people with asthma.
2 Why do people with asthma need inhalers?
3 Design a poster for a sports centre which explains the symptoms of asthma.
4 What two things can bring on an asthma attack?
5 List the symptoms of asthma. Explain how these can affect your life.

Keywords

asthma

airways

symptom

inhaler

reliever

preventer

protector

Gasping for breath

7.4 Smoking

Why is smoking dangerous?

These protesters feel very strongly about smoking! They feel that it should be banned from all public places to protect non-smokers. People who do not smoke may be 'passive' smokers if they live with other people who smoke. Passive smoking is harmful too.

The arrow in this X-ray points to a cancer in the lung. Scientists have proved that certain chemicals in **tobacco** smoke cause cancer. This is why there is a warning on every cigarette packet.

Tar - This clogs the lungs reducing their volume and the speed that people can breathe in and out. Colds, bronchitis and lung diseases are much more likely.

Nicotine - an **addictive** drug that raises the heart rate.

Hydrogen Cyanide - a poisonous gas, used to execute condemned prisoners in the USA.

Carbon monoxide - a poisonous gas which stops red blood cells carring oxygen

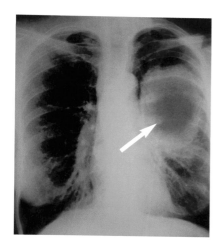

Chance of a child developing a bad cough if parents smoke

Cigarettes smoked by parent per day	Sweden	Poland	Estonia
0	1.0	1.0	1.0
1–9	0.67	1.38	1.8
9+	1.4	2.88	4.27

Questions

1 Your friend has asked you to help him stop smoking. How would you do this?

2 List three dangerous chemicals found in cigarettes.

3 What is the increased risk of a coughing fit for children in Estonia whose parents smoke more than nine cigarettes a day?

4 What is surprising about the data from Sweden?

5 Do you think doctors in Sweden would tell parents to smoke to reduce the chances of their children getting coughing fits? Explain your answer.

6 Suggest two reasons why the results in Sweden are different from those in Estonia.

Keywords

tobacco

nicotine

addictive

tar

Hydrogen Cyanide

Carbon monoxide

7 Data response: Road traffic and asthma

Carbon dioxide – helps to create global warming.

Nitrogen oxides – irritate the lungs of people living near roads and help to create acid rain.

Particulates – tiny lumps of soot that may be linked to lung disease and allergies.

Asthma attacks and distance of home from a busy road

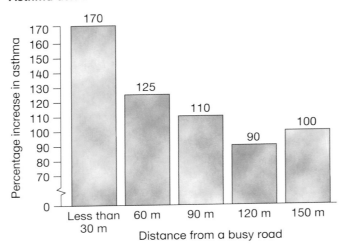

Asthma attacks per 100,000 people in children and pensioners since 1996

Males	1996	1998	2001	2003
Less than 15	338	260	167	123
65+	52	45	41	32
Females	**1996**	**1998**	**2001**	**2003**
Less than 15	234	190	120	104
65+	65	58	46	41

Chance of a child visiting the doctor with asthma if parents smoke

Year of study	Children in study	Chance of child of non-smokers	Chance of a child of smokers
1986	8000	1	2
1990	770	1	1.1
1992	774	1	2.5

Data response

1 List the main pollutants found near a busy road.

2 Which children have the highest risk of asthma?

3 What was the risk for children living approximately 90 m from a major road?

4 Do you think there is a link between asthma and road traffic?

Gasping for breath

5 Why is it difficult to prove that road traffic causes asthma?

6 What is surprising about the result for children living 120 m from a busy road?

7 Give three factors that might affect how likely you are to get asthma.

8 Is the rate of asthma going up or down?

9 Are young children or pensioners more likely to suffer from asthma?

10 Which of the studies in seem most reliable? Why?

Research

To collect a sample of dust with a piece of sticky tape, press the sticky side of the tape onto a flat surface, then peel it off. The dust is trapped on the tape. You can then use a microscope to count the number of dust particles per piece of tape.

10 Plan an investigation to find out if areas near roads are more dusty than other areas.

11 Alternatively, carry out a survey of your school or neighbourhood. Which areas have the most dust?

Presentation

12 Prepare a presentation for parents who have been told their son has asthma. You should cover the main facts and be encouraging. Do not frighten them! Make clear what they should do if their son has an asthma attack.

Learning progress

I know:

- Narrowing of the airways causes asthma. Air pollution and some allergies may cause asthma. An inhaler can relieve and prevent the symptoms of asthma.

- Different people have different lung volumes. These may be affected by asthma and smoking.

- Smoking can cause heart diseases and damage the lungs. Passive smoking occurs when a non-smoker breathes in smoke from other people's cigarettes.

- Oxygen is needed to get energy from food and that the body takes in oxygen through the lungs. Carbon dioxide produced by respiration leaves the body through the lungs. During exercise the breathing rate rises to supply more oxygen to the muscles and to take away the extra carbon dioxide.

I can:

- Label the windpipe, lungs and ribs on a diagram of the thorax.

- Test for carbon dioxide using limewater.

- Test for water vapour using a mirror or cobalt chloride paper.

- Interpret data about exercise and breathing rates.

8.1 Tie-dyed and tasteful

How can we make coloured fabric?

Very colourful – but probably not suitable for work!
Many of these fabrics started out as plain white and were
coloured with dyes.

Woad is a plant
that can be used
to make blue dye.
Ancient British
warriors coloured
their skin with the
dye from woad to
frighten away
invading
Romans.

A **dye** is a substance that can change the colour of
something else. Many traditional dyes come from a
plant or vegetable. Onion skins can dye white cotton
cloth yellow. Your jeans were probably coloured with
a blue dye called **indigo** which is also made from a
plant. As well as these **natural** dyes, there are many
artificial dyes which tend to provide the bright
colours in clothes.

Sometimes a substance is added to the dye solution to help the dye
stick to the cloth. This is called a **mordant**. Here are some results
obtained when cotton cloth was heated with water containing
onion skins.

	Experiment 1: salt added	Experiment 2: no salt added
Temperature (°C)	Dye absorbed (%)	Dye absorbed (%)
60	15	8
80	20	10
100	25	12

Questions

1 What is a dye?

2 What do these results tell you about the best temperature for
dyeing cloth?

3 What is a mordant?

4 Is salt a mordant for the dye in onion skins? Explain your
answer.

5 Plan an investigation to see which of the following would dye
cloth well: beetroot, grass, milk, potato, plain yoghurt,
raspberries.

Keywords

dye

indigo

natural

artificial

mordant

Acids and alkalis

8.2 Acid or alkali?

What is an indicator?

Many Indian foods contain **turmeric**, a natural yellow colour made from the root of a plant. Turmeric changes colour in an **acid** or in an **alkali**. A dye which changes colour when it goes from acid to alkali is called an **indicator**. In an acid, turmeric is orangey yellow. In an alkali, turmeric turns pink.

Scientists use **litmus paper** to detect acids and alkalis. Litmus is a kind of moss that grows in cold parts of the world. The dye is extracted and the solution is soaked into filter paper. All acids turn litmus paper pink.

	Acid	Alkali
Taste	Sour	
Litmus paper	Pink	Blue
Turmeric paper	Orangey-yellow	Pink
Universal indicator	Orange	Blue
Examples	Vinegar, lemon juice, hydrochloric acid	Washing soda, sodium hydroxide, many soaps

But solutions are not just acid or alkaline – some are very strongly acid while others are only just acid. Scientists use a scale called the **pH scale** to measure the acidity or alkalinity of a solution. The chart shows the pH for some different solutions. A special indicator called **universal indicator** (UI) is used to check for pH. UI has a different colour for every pH value.

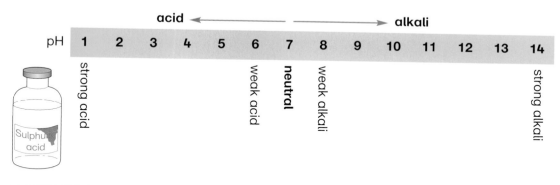

acid ← → alkali

| pH | 1 | 2 | 3 | 4 | 5 | 6 | 7 | 8 | 9 | 10 | 11 | 12 | 13 | 14 |

strong acid · weak acid · neutral · weak alkali · strong alkali

Sulphuric acid

Sodium hydroxide

Questions

1 What colour does litmus paper go in an acid?

2 What colour does litmus paper go in an alkali?

3 How could you use litmus paper to see which foods are acids?

4 A piece of UI paper goes green in a solution. What is the pH of the solution?

5 How can you tell which of your favourite drinks are acids?

6 Why is UI paper more useful than litmus paper for telling the pH of a solution?

Keywords

turmeric

acid

alkali

indicator

litmus paper

pH scale

universal indicator

8.3 Reactions of acids

How do acids react?

All **acids** react in similar ways. This allows us to predict what might happen when we react an acid with an unknown chemical.

Reactions with metals

Acids dissolve many **metals** and give off the gas hydrogen. Hydrogen burns with a popping sound. Not all metals react this way and sometimes the reaction is so slow that you can only see it after many years.

Reactions with carbonates

Acids react quickly with **carbonates** to produce the gas carbon dioxide. We can see this reaction easily because the powdered carbonate fizzes as the gas is given off.

Reactions with alkalis

When acids and **alkalis** react together they form a **neutral** solution. The reaction is called **neutralisation**. Neutralisation produces a solution which is not alkaline or acid. Pure water is neutral.

Testing for hydrogen

Light the gas and it will burn with a popping sound. Sometimes you can see droplets of moisture where the hydrogen has burnt because burning hydrogen in air produces water.

Testing for carbon dioxide

The gas will put out a lighted splint. It will also turn limewater milky when it bubbles through it.

Questions

1 What gas is made when an acid reacts with a metal?

2 What gas is made when an acid reacts with a carbonate?

3 What two types of chemicals do you need for a neutralisation reaction?

4 A gas burns with a popping sound. What gas is it?

5 How could you test for carbon dioxide?

6 An acid makes a white powder fizz. The gas given off turns limewater milky. What sort of chemical is the white powder? How can you tell?

Keywords

acid

metal

carbonate

alkali

neutral

neutralisation

8.4 Using neutralisation

How can we use neutralisation?

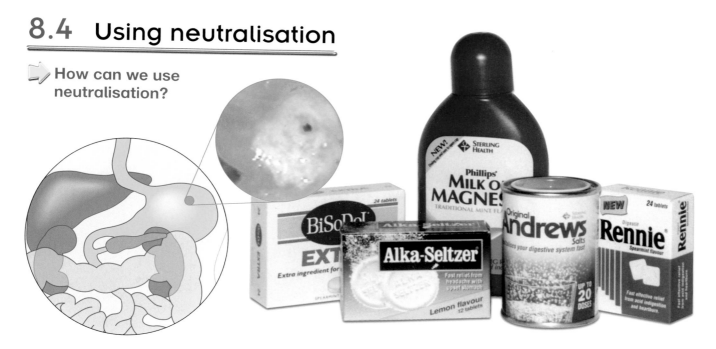

Your stomach contains about one litre of **hydrochloric acid**. This breaks your food down into useful chemicals. Too much acid in your stomach can cause **indigestion**. The picture shows damage to the stomach wall caused by acid. Indigestion tablets contain a weak alkali called **bicarbonate of soda**. When acids and alkalis react together they form a **neutral** solution. The reaction is called **neutralisation**. As the acid is removed by this reaction the pain should fade.

The farmer is using a neutralisation reaction to control the acidity of the soil. He adds **lime** to the soil. This helps to neutralise the acid in the soil and makes it easier for plants to grow.

Questions

1 What is a neutral solution? Give one example.
2 What colour will a piece of red litmus paper go in a neutral solution?
3 What happens when indigestion tablets are added to hydrochloric acid?
4 Plan an investigation to see which indigestion tablets are the best.
5 Why are indigestion tablets sometimes called antacids?
6 Why do farmers add lime to their soil?

Keywords

hydrochloric acid

indigestion

bicarbonate of soda

neutral

neutralisation

lime

8 Data response: Stomach ache

Things that increase acid production in the stomach

Smoking

Coffee – especially black coffee

Some spicy foods

Vinegar and other acidic foods

Aspirin

Some bacteria

Stress and rushing

Antacid

Calcium carbonate 92g; sodium hydrogen carbonate 7g; guar gum 1g; flavouring (peppermint)

DOSAGE:
Take two tablets as required.

ChewAndHurl

Extract of ginseng 10g; calcium carbonate 85g; flavourings (peppermint, garden samphire, yak butter); sweeteners (yam sugar)

DOSAGE:
Chew four tablets using a side to side action. Swallow the mixture produced with a glass of mineral water if required.

Peptidol

magnesium carbonate 30g; calcium carbonate 65g; sodium hydrogen carbonate 4g; flavourings (peppermint oil, artificial sweetener)

Take one 5ml teaspoonful as required.
No more than 20ml in 24 hours.

TumEeze

Calcium carbonate 95g; sodium hydrogen carbonate 5g; peppermint oil, colourings

DOSAGE:
Take two tablets in water when discomfort begins.

Data response

1 Which indigestion remedy has the most alkali?

2 Which indigestion remedy has the least alkali?

3 Which indigestion remedy needs to be swallowed in water?

4 Which remedy costs the most?

5 What is wrong with taking indigestion remedies every day?

6 Draw a bar chart to show the amounts of alkali in each type of indigestion remedy.

7 Nathan is a coffee-drinking smoker working in a hectic office in the city. His job is extremely stressful and he often misses his lunch to carry on working at his desk. He keeps getting indigestion and is asking for advice. What do you suggest? Why?

8 Plan and carry out an investigation to discover how much acid a range of indigestion remedies can neutralise.

Presentation

9 Design the packaging for a new indigestion treatment. The treatment uses two tablets which you take when you start to feel pain. On your packaging you must include pictures and text to explain:

- how the tablets work
- why you should not take more than eight tablets in a day
- why you should see your doctor if the pain lasts more than a week.

Make your packaging colourful and attractive. Remember – it has to stand out from other indigestion remedies!

Learning progress

I know:

- Acids or alkalis change the colour of some dyes. These dyes are called indicators. Litmus is blue in alkalis and red in acids. Universal indicator is red, orange or yellow in acids, green in neutral solution and dark blue in alkaline solutions.

- pH is a measure of acidity or alkalinity and it ranges from pH1 (very acid) to pH14 (very alkaline). Pure water is pH7 and is neutral.

- Acids fizz with carbonates to make carbon dioxide gas. Acids react with metals like magnesium and zinc to make hydrogen.

- A neutralisation reaction is a reaction between an acid and an alkali to produce a neutral solution. Neutralisation reactions can be used to cure indigestion and reduce the acidity of soils.

I can:

- Use litmus to identify solutions that are acidic, alkaline or neutral.
- Use Universal Indicator to find the pH of a solution.
- Test for carbon dioxide using limewater and hydrogen by watching it burn with a popping sound.

9.1 Mammoth burgers all round!

What is a chemical reaction?

This tribesman in Tibet is cooking food in the same way as people have been doing it for years. The astronauts are enjoying a hi tech, pre-cooked feast of space age mushy protein and vitamins. Which would you prefer to eat?

Cooking changes the texture and flavour of food. It often makes food easier to digest and kills dangerous microbes. Some foods are actually almost poisonous if eaten raw. Kidney beans will kill you unless you boil them! A potato gets softer and the taste improves when you cook it.

Cooking is a good example of a **chemical reaction**. Burning and glue-setting are also chemical reactions. The **reactants** are what you start with and the **products** are the substances the reaction makes. In a chemical reaction:

- the products are very different from the reactants
- the change cannot easily be undone.

Questions

1 List three foods that you can eat raw.
2 List two foods you have to cook to make them worth eating.
3 List three reasons why food is cooked.
4 What is a reactant?
5 List two things that are true about chemical reactions.
6 Ice melting is not usually called a chemical reaction. Why not?
7 Many chemical reactions go more quickly if they are warmed up. Plan an investigation to find out if glue sets more quickly if it is heated gently.

Keywords

chemical reaction

reactant

product

9.2 Kitchen nightmares?

What is the best way to cook food?

Black and crispy on the outside but pink and juicy inside! Cooking in this sort of kitchen is not easy – not too many pots to wash up though! Different cooking methods have different advantages and disadvantages. Which is best? It depends on the food you're cooking.

Cooking method	Types of foods	Advantages	Disadvantages
Boiling	Meats, vegetables, rice	Easy	Can destroy the flavour
Frying	Meat, chopped vegetables	Quick	Can add fat to food – which is not healthy
Grilling	Meat	Cooks food without adding fat	Not all foods can be grilled
Steaming	Vegetables, rice	Preserves goodness in foods	Not suitable for all foods
Microwaving	Most foods	Very quick and energy efficient	Microwaved food may not taste as good as food cooked in a normal oven
Conventional oven	Most foods	Can take a long time	Ovens can be expensive to buy and run

Cooking pasta like spaghetti is easy. You just add it to boiling water. But how long should you cook it? Not long enough and the pasta is hard. Too long and it goes mushy.

Cooking time (mins)	Spaghetti	Macaroni	Noodles
3	Nearly raw!	Nearly raw!	Too hard
4	Too hard	Nearly raw!	A bit hard
5	Too hard	Too hard	About right
6	About right	Too hard	A bit soft
7	A bit soft	About right	Far too soft
8	Far too soft	About right	Far too soft
9	Far too soft	Too soft	Looks like white soup!
10	Looks like white soup!	Far too soft	Looks like white soup!

Questions

1 Give one advantage of microwave ovens.

2 Give one disadvantage of grilling.

3 Why is it a good idea to avoid frying foods if you are trying to lose weight?

4 How long should you cook spaghetti?

5 Which cooks more quickly: spaghetti, macaroni or noodles?

6 Plan an investigation to see how long you need to cook rice.

Keywords

boiling

frying

grilling

steaming

microwaving

conventional oven

9.3 Getting fizzical!

Why is carbon dioxide useful?

Champagne bubbles are pure carbon dioxide. The gas bubbles are dissolved in the drink and when they rise up they make the drink fizzy. When they have all risen to the surface the drink tastes flat – it is not fizzy any more.

Yeast gives champagne, and beer, its fizz. Yeast is a microorganism that converts sugar to alcohol and carbon dioxide. This reaction is called **fermentation**.

sugar → alcohol + carbon dioxide

Brewers keep the fermenting liquid warm to help the yeast work. After a while the yeast settles out and the beer is sealed into bottles.

Self-raising flour is used in many cake recipes. Self-raising powder contains a chemical which gives out carbon dioxide when it gets hot. The carbon dioxide makes the cake rise. A good muffin is full of carbon dioxide **gas**! We can show the **chemical reaction** as a word equation:

baking powder → carbon dioxide + sodium carbonate

Questions

1 What two things have to happen for a chemical reaction to take place?

2 Why do these happen?

3 List examples of chemical reactions that occur in your kitchen.

4 What does fermentation mean?

5 How could you measure the amount of carbon dioxide given off when baking powder is used?

6 Plan an investigation to find out which brand of baking powder is best.

Keywords

fermentation

gas

chemical reaction

Cooking and cleaning

9.4 Cleaning up

What is the difference between soaps and detergent?

The music at the Slovenian hard rock festival was so bad that these people decided to roll around in the mud instead! It will take more than a hose and water to clean them up!

Soaps are made from animal **fats** or plant **oils** heated with an alkali called sodium hydroxide. Soaps are expensive to make and can form **scum** with some types of water. You might have seen scum as a sticky white ring around the bowl or bath.

Detergents are cheaper to make than soaps and do not form scum. They are made from chemicals produced from crude oil.

Some washing powders contain **enzymes**. These help to digest away stains that contain **protein**, such as egg yolk and blood.

Time needed to clean a blackcurrant juice stain with Scotto Soap Powder

Temperature (°C)	Time needed (mins)
40	30
50	20
60	10

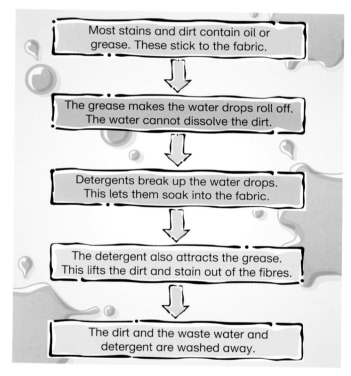

Most stains and dirt contain oil or grease. These stick to the fabric.

⬇

The grease makes the water drops roll off. The water cannot dissolve the dirt.

⬇

Detergents break up the water drops. This lets them soak into the fabric.

⬇

The detergent also attracts the grease. This lifts the dirt and stain out of the fibres.

⬇

The dirt and the waste water and detergent are washed away.

Questions

1 Give two differences between soap and detergents.

2 Explain how detergents work.

3 Draw a bar chart to show the time needed to clean blackcurrant juice using Scotto at different temperatures.

4 Why don't we always boil clothes when we wash them to make sure they are clean?

5 The green outfits worn by surgeons in operating theatres are not just washed. They are boiled. Why?

Keywords

soap

fats

oils

scum

detergent

enzyme

protein

9 Data response: Fast foods?

Noodles, corn on the cob, squid, rice and soya bean curd are all available at this market in Beijing, China. Good food – and cheap! You can get McDonalds burgers as well – but only in a shop and it's much more expensive.

Food	Cooking method	Time to cook potatoes (minutes)
Baked potatoes	Oven	50
Baked potatoes	Microwave oven	15
Oven chips	Oven	15
Oven chips	Grill	5
Oven chips	Microwave	4

Potato	Cost per kg
Raw potatoes	£0.50
Oven chips	£1.35
Microwave chips	£4.50
Potato croquettes	£6.00

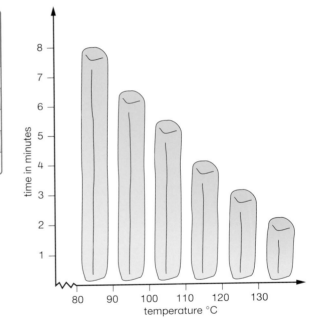

Data response

1 What is the quickest way to cook potatoes?

2 How long does it take to cook oven chips under the grill?

3 Draw a chart to show the cost of the different types of potatoes.

4 How long does it take to cook chips in oil at 103°C?

5 List the changes that occur when raw potato chips are cooked.

6 Are the changes you listed in question 5 chemical changes? Give a reason for your answer.

Cooking and cleaning

7 Some types of crisps say they have less fat and energy to make them healthier. Plan an investigation to see how much energy different brands of crisps contain.

8 Which cooking method is best for each of these places? Prepare a presentation showing the advantages and disadvantages for each.
- a posh flat in Kensington London
- camping at the Glastonbury festival
- a stall in Beijing's Snack Street – look at the picture to get some clues!

Learning progress

I know:

- There are many ways to cook food and that these have different advantages and disadvantages.

- Food is cooked to improve the texture and taste, make it easier to digest and to kill microbes in the food.

- Cooking food is an example of a chemical change. A chemical change takes place when a new substance forms and the process is not reversible.

- How to investigate changes to food when it is cooked in different ways.

- Baking powder gives out carbon dioxide when it is heated. It is used to make cakes and dough rise.

- Yeast makes carbon dioxide by fermentation which makes bread rise. Yeast also makes alcohol in beers.

- Acids break down carbonates to give out carbon dioxide in a 'fizzing' reaction.

- Soap is made from animal fat or plant oils. Synthetic detergents are made from chemicals found in crude oil. Enzymes are added to washing powders to help digest stains like blood and egg which contain protein.

- Detergents work by breaking up water droplets to help them get into the fabric and wash away the dirt. Detergents also attract the grease which sticks the dirt to the fabric.

- How to interpret washing labels on clothes.

I can:

- Carry out a test to show the presence of carbon dioxide.
- Use a Bunsen burner safely.

Respond • Research • Present

10.1 Paints and pigments

What is a pigment?

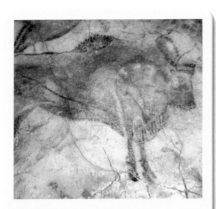

Ancient cave paintings used ash and powdered rocks. The ancient artists probably mixed the powders with animal fat to make it stick to the rock. They may have sprayed the **paint** onto the rock through straws.

Egyptian pigments included powdered rocks like **azurite** (blue) and **malachite** (green). They even used a pigment called **cochineal** (red) which they made from crushed beetles!

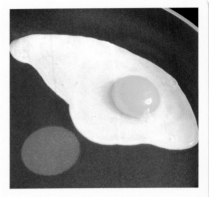

The red spot in this frying pan uses **thermochromic** paint. It changes colour at different temperatures. When it turns red you know the frying pan is the perfect temperature for cooking bacon and eggs!

Oil **paints** have pigments mixed with oil. A **solvent** helps to dissolve the oil to keep it liquid when you use it. Water-based paints like emulsions for walls use pigments that dissolve in water. A kind of thin glue acts as the binding agent.

A **pigment** is a coloured substance. These pigments are mixed with liquids to make paints. A modern paint uses:

- pigments: many are now made by chemists
- binding agents: these help the pigment to stick to the thing you want to paint
- solvents: these keep the paint liquid while you use it. When the solvent evaporates the paint dries.

Paints can be used to decorate surfaces or to protect them. Gloss paint on window frames keeps water away from the wood to stop it rotting. Paint on cars stops the metal from rusting.

Questions

1 What was the blue pigment the Egyptians used?
2 Who used pigments made from ash?
3 What colour is made from crushed beetles?
4 Why does paint need a binding agent?
5 What is special about a thermochromic pigment?
6 Think of three things that could use thermochromic pigments.

Keywords

paint
azurite
malachite
cochineal
thermochromic
solvent
pigment

Colours and smells

10.2 Paintball!

How do paintballs work?

Good fun or a bit sad?
Grown men run around
the woods shooting balls
of paint at each other!
The paintball guns use a
blast of air to shoot the
ball. When it hits the
target the soft outer skin
of the ball breaks and the
paint splashes out.

Looking after your balls!

▶ **Keep the paintballs in a dry place.**

▶ **Do not let the temperature rise above 30°C**

▶ **Do not let the temperature drop below 5°C**

▶ **Only buy enough paintballs for one or two games. Fresh balls are better than old ones.**

Jelly-like outer layer
– splits when it hits the target

Pigments
– the coloured powder in the ball

Binding medium
– helps make the paint
stick to the target and
stops the pigment
clumping together

Questions

1 What part of the paintball is coloured?

2 Why is the paint in a paintball **water-soluble**?

3 What is a **binding medium**?

4 A fault in the paintball factory produced paintballs with skins
that were four times as thick as normal. Why might this make
the paintballs useless?

5 Why should you store paintballs in a dry place?

6 Plan an investigation to find out how temperatures below
freezing affect paintballs.

Keywords

water-soluble

binding medium

10.3 Dissolving stuff

How do solvents help to clean things?

This will take a while to clean up! This is because oil does not dissolve in water. Unfortunately, the solvents that can dissolve oil can also damage the skin.

The thing the **solvent** dissolves is called the **solute**. When the solute dissolves in the solvent the liquid that is made is called a **solution**. When the solvent dries out the solute is left behind.

Stain	Solvent	Dangers
Gloss paints	**White spirit** Turps	Burns very easily
Nail varnish	Nail varnish remover	Burns easily
Waxes and grease	**Trichloroethane Paraffin Meths**	**Toxic** fumes
Crude oil	White spirit Some powerful detergents	Can dissolve the oils that protect the skin

Choosing a solvent is not always easy. The table shows some solvents and the solutes they can dissolve. One solvent cannot dissolve everything. Many solvents are powerful chemicals that can be dangerous.

Questions

1 What is a solvent?
2 Why do people have to be careful when they use trichloroethane indoors?
3 Which solvent could I use to clean gloss paint from paintbrushes?
4 People warm water to help it to dissolve salt more easily. Why would this be a very dangerous thing to do with meths?
5 Plan an investigation to find the best solvent to clean ink from white cloth.
6 Give two advantages of modern paints that use water-soluble pigments rather than oil-soluble ones.

Keywords

solvent
solute
solution
white spirit
trichloroethane
paraffin
meths
toxic

Colours and smells

Perfumes and pongs

How can you make a perfume?

These women will almost certainly have smeared something made from dead deer on their skin. Many modern **perfumes** use **musk**. To get the musk from the glands the deer must be killed and cut open. Musk is three times as expensive as solid gold!

Other perfumes can be made from plants. **Steam distillation** can extract perfumes from lavender flowers, orange peel and patchouli leaves. Some perfumes are made by chemists in laboratories.

A perfume has to smell nice. It must also evaporate easily. You can only smell the perfume when it is in the air.

Some perfumes are tested on animals. By 2009 many **animal tests** for **cosmetics** will be banned in the EU.

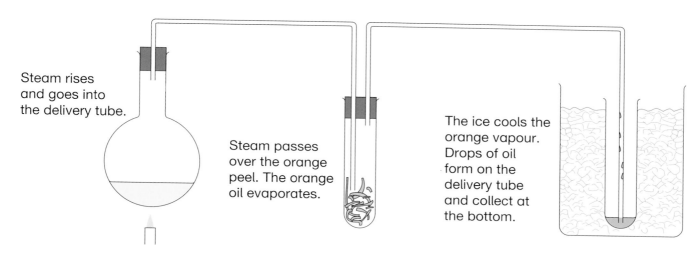

Steam rises and goes into the delivery tube.

Steam passes over the orange peel. The orange oil evaporates.

The ice cools the orange vapour. Drops of oil form on the delivery tube and collect at the bottom.

Questions

1 Why do you need the ice in the beaker?

2 Why not heat the orange peel with a Bunsen burner instead of using steam?

3 Why does musk in perfumes threaten musk deer survival?

4 List three plants that can be used to make perfumes.

5 Give two reasons why perfumes need to be tested before they can be sold.

6 Why do perfumes have to evaporate easily?

Keywords

perfume

musk

steam distillation

animal testing

cosmetics

Goths! Don't you love their cheerful little faces? And their painted nails? And the stroppy, depressing music... But usually it passes. And then the black paint must be covered up with something more cheerful – but which paint is best?

The table below shows the walls of a goth bedroom after one and two coats of white paint. How many coats are needed to cover up the cheery Death Rock Survivors drawing?

Paint	Cost for 2.5l	Coverage in square metres	Wash brushes in
Delux	£7.99	25–30	water
Royal	£7.59	24–28	water
D + B own brand	£4.99	20	water
Paintbase	£6.99	27–30	water
SuperCover	£11.99	30–35	paint thinner

Paint	One coat	Second coat
Delux	DEATH ROCK SURVIVORS	
Royal	DEATH ROCK SURVIVORS	
D + B own brand	DEATH ROCK SURVIVORS	
Paintbase	DEATH ROCK SURVIVORS	
SuperCover		

Data response

1 Which is the cheapest paint?

2 Which three brands cost more than £7.00 per tin?

3 Work out the cost of each brand per litre.

4 The figures on the tins of paint give a range, not an exact figure for coverage. Why?

5 How many tins of Paintbase would you need to buy to give every wall two coats?

6 SuperCover claims that it covers in one coat. Does the evidence support this claim?

7 Which paint would be the cheapest option to completely repaint the bedroom walls?

8 Give one disadvantage of SuperCover besides the cost.

Research

7 Plan an investigation to find out how well a particular paint brand covers dark coloured wallpaper. Explain how you would measure how well the paint covered the paper.

Presentation

8 Modern paints often use water instead of other solvents. This means the brushes are easier to clean. It also reduces the fumes given off by the paint while you are using it and while it dries. Prepare a leaflet to explain to consumers why this is a good thing.

Learning progress

I know:

- A pigment is a coloured substance used in paint. Paints contain a solvent, a binding medium and pigment. Paints are used to decorate and protect surfaces.

- Some paints can change colour when heated or cooled. These are called thermochromic paints and are used in some cooking pans.

- Oil paints have pigment dispersed in oil and a solvent to dissolve the oil. Water-based paints have pigments dissolved in a mixture of water and a binder such as glue.

- Solvents can be used to remove stains such as paints or nail varnish. A solute is a substance that dissolves in a solvent to form a solution.

- Many cosmetics can be made from natural sources (for example, Norfolk lavender). The essential oils in lavender can be collected by steam distillation.

- A perfume must smell nice, evaporate easily and not irritate the skin. Many perfumes are made from natural sources including orange peel, rose petals and musk glands from musk deer. Some perfumes are made by chemists, often using weak acids. All perfumes and cosmetics must be tested for safety before they are put on sale. Some people will not buy perfumes or cosmetics tested on animals.

I can:

- Make an artificial perfume.
- Make a paint and prove that it works.

11.1 Three metals

 Why are metals useful?

You can find tiny specks of pure **gold** in the rivers of North Wales. Because gold is so dense it tends to settle at the bottom. Some people pan for gold by swirling the stones and grit from the river bed in a plate. The small particles of gold sparkle in the light and can be collected – if you're lucky!

Gold is a precious metal. In 2005, 1 gram of gold cost roughly £28. That's a speck of gold roughly the same size as a grain of sand! At the same time, all the iron in a car engine cost less than £25.

Iron is a useful metal. It is cheap, strong and easy to use. Unfortunately, iron **rusts** in air. It changes from a strong, shiny metal into a crumbly brown crystal. Iron must be painted to protect it from air and damp. We have to heat rocks containing iron to a high temperature to get the iron out.

Aluminium is a strong, light metal. Two men can carry this caravan shell! But it is very expensive. The **electricity** used to make one roll of kitchen foil could boil over 500 kettles of water! Before we could make electricity we could not use aluminium at all. Now it is used for kitchen foil, laptop computer cases, aircraft and even some cars. Aluminium does not rust.

All metals are shiny and can be beaten into flat sheets. They also all let heat and electricity pass easily through them.

Questions

1 List four things that are true about gold and iron.

2 Give two differences between gold and aluminium.

3 Why do you think that metal workers used gold long before iron?

4 How would you recognise tiny fragments of gold in river gravel?

5 How much is the 1575g of gold in the buckle at the top of the page worth at 2005 prices?

Keywords

gold

iron

rust

aluminium

electricity

Heavy metal?

11.2 Copper

 Why is recycling copper a good idea?

The Statue of Liberty is made of **copper** and is already over 100 years old. Copper is a useful metal. It exists in nature as an **ore**. An ore is a chemical that contains a metal and something else. **Malachite** is a green copper ore. How can you get copper out of malachite?

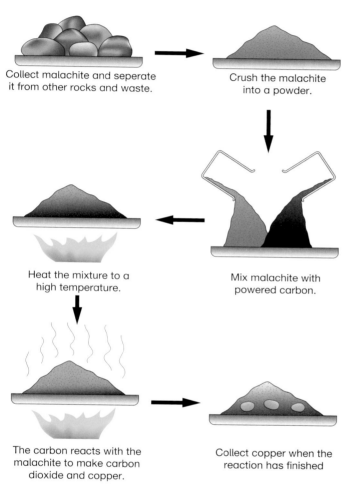

Collect malachite and seperate it from other rocks and waste.

Crush the malachite into a powder.

Mix malachite with powered carbon.

Heat the mixture to a high temperature.

The carbon reacts with the malachite to make carbon dioxide and copper.

Collect copper when the reaction has finished

This uses a lot of energy. **Recycling** copper is much cheaper. About half of the copper used in the USA every year comes from recycling. Copper can be recycled by:

- melting the scrap to make bars of copper
- using electricity to produce very pure copper.

Copper recycling values

Type of scrap	Value (£ per kg)
Old copper hot water tanks	1.46
Bright copper wire with no insulation	1.49
Scrap insulated copper wire from mains leads	0.32
Soldered copper water pipe	1.13

Questions

1 What is an ore?

2 Name one copper ore.

3 Why is recycling copper cheaper than making new copper from ore?

4 Give two safety warnings for someone heating malachite in a chemistry laboratory.

5 Draw a bar chart to show the value of different types of copper scrap.

6 Which is worth more money; 3 tonne of old hot water tanks or 13 tonne of old mains cable?

Keywords

copper

ore

malachite

recycling

11.3 Pure or plated?

> How can you make cheap jewellery look expensive?

Silver is much cheaper than gold – but more expensive than steel. Manufacturers coat cheap jewellery with metals like silver, gold or platinum to make it look **expensive**. There are two ways to do this:

a Dip the piece in molten gold, silver or platinum, pull it out and let a layer of precious metal solidify onto the cheap metal jewellery. This gives a thick, uneven **coating** of precious metal.

b A better method is **electroplating**. Electroplating produces a thin, even coating of the precious metal.

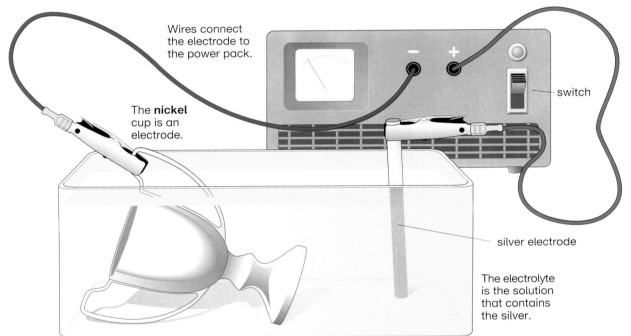

Wires connect the electrode to the power pack.

The **nickel** cup is an electrode.

switch

silver electrode

The electrolyte is the solution that contains the silver.

Electrolysis can purify metals like copper. If you use a positive electrode of impure copper it will slowly dissolve away. However, the copper that sticks to the negative electrode is pure. This is because impurities and other metals in the solution are not attracted to the electrode.

Questions

1 Give two ways to coat a metal ring with gold.
2 What is an electrode?
3 Is the nickel cup above the positive or negative electrode?
4 What is the electrolyte in this experiment?
5 What might affect the thickness of silver on the cup?
6 Why is a thin, even coating of precious metal better than a thick, uneven coating?

Keywords

expensive
coating
electroplating
nickel

Heavy metal?

11.4 Rust bucket

What is the problem with iron?

The trouble with **iron** is that it **rusts**. Moisture and **oxygen** in the air attack the metal and convert it into a brownish-orange crystal. This makes it very brittle and it can snap. Unfortunately, salt speeds up **corrosion**. The Forth Rail Bridge is over a large river estuary and salt from the sea water makes the bridge rust even more quickly.

The Forth Rail Bridge is made of **steel** and needs to be painted to stop it from rusting. At one time it took so long to paint that as soon as the team got to the end of the bridge they had to start again!

Moisture and oxygen react with the surface of the metal

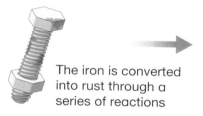
The iron is converted into rust through a series of reactions

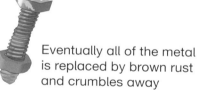
Eventually all of the metal is replaced by brown rust and crumbles away

Cars contain a lot of iron and steel. This rusts and the car is ruined. Would it be better to build cars out of a metal like **aluminium** that does not rust?

Metal	Does it rust?	How strong is it?	How light is it?	Cost
Iron	Yes	★★★★	★★	★★
Aluminium	No	★★★★★	★★★★	★★★★

The more stars the better/higher.

Questions

1 Write a sentence containing the word 'corrosion'.
2 What three substances are needed to make rust?
3 How is the Forth Bridge protected from rust?
4 Give two advantages of aluminium over iron for making cars.
5 Give one disadvantage of aluminium for making cars.
6 Cars with aluminium bodies tend to be lighter in weight than steel cars. Give one advantage of this not mentioned on this page.

Keywords

iron

rust

oxygen

corrosion

steel

aluminium

11 Data response: Pierce that!

If only his mother could see him now! The collar looks comfortable enough – if you like that sort of thing but the nose ring and lip piercing must have hurt. The metal must be specially treated so that it does not cause allergic reactions.

Metal	Does it rust?	Does it produce an allergic reaction?	Cost/£ per kg
Iron	Yes – quickly	Yes	0.65
Stainless steel	No	Very rarely	1.25
Chromium steel	No	Rarely	1.80
Copper	Yes	Yes	2.90
Aluminium	No	Sometimes	1.50
Silver	Yes – but slowly	Sometimes	170.00
Gold	No	Never	1500.00

Data response

1 Which metal never causes an allergic reaction?

2 Explain why iron is not used for body piercings.

3 Which metals cost more than £1.50 per gram?

4 A nose stud contains 15 g of stainless steel. How much does the metal cost?

5 How much would a gold stud of the same weight cost?

6 Some metal piercings are coated with gold. Why?

7 Why is wood not used for body piercings?

Research

8 Plan an investigation to find out how quickly iron rusts in different conditions. Test the effect on iron of water, salt and temperature.

Presentation

9 Metals are everywhere in our modern world. We depend on steel in buildings and bridges, cars and trains, machines like fridges and cookers and even in packaging for some foods. Imagine a bacterium is created accidentally in a laboratory that can digest iron. It converts shiny metal into a grey powder in only a few days. Prepare a news report to show what has happened two years after the bacterium infected metals in a big city like London or Birmingham.

Learning progress

I know:

- Unreactive metal like gold can be found unreacted in the Earth. It can be collected from stream and river beds by panning.

- Gold, silver and platinum are expensive and shiny heavy metals. Because they do not react easily they are used to make jewellery. Some cheap jewellery is coated in gold to prevent allergic reactions to the cheaper metal it is made from.

- Copper can be extracted by heating its ore with carbon. Recycling copper is cheaper than making copper and saves resources.

- Electroplating uses an electric current to coat cheap metals with silver, gold or platinum. These plated metals can be used in jewellery, silver-plated cutlery or chromium-plated steel.

- Rusting needs iron, water and oxygen. It is speeded up by salt water.

- Aluminium is used in some cars because it does not rust and is very light and strong. One disadvantage of aluminium is that it is much more expensive than steel.

- Iron and steel are magnetic. Copper, aluminium, gold and silver are not.

I can:

- Extract a sample of copper from its ore.
- Use a magnet to tell the difference between iron and aluminium.

Fibres and fabrics

12.1 Worth millions!

What is the difference between fibres and fabrics?

These clothes are made from different **fabrics**. Some of the fabrics are made from **threads** woven together. Others seem to be a sort of plastic. Some even have metal threads woven into them or jewels sewn onto them to make them sparkle and look more glamorous.

A fabric is a flat sheet. In the past these sheets were made of threads woven together. Nowadays we can produce flat plastic or rubber sheets.

In woven fabrics the properties of the fabric depend on the thread used to make them. These threads are made of even thinner **fibres** twisted together.

There are two sorts of fibre: **natural** and **artificial**.

Natural	Artificial
Silk, wool, mohair, cotton, linen	Acrylic, lycra, nylon, polyester

Fibre	Properties
Acrylic	Strong, soft and warm
Lycra	Very stretchy, springs back into shape
Nylon	Stretchy, strong, tough
Polyester	Quick-drying, tough, blends well with other fibres
Wool	Stretchy, soft, warm
Cotton	Stretchy, can be cool or warm, absorbs water

Questions

1 What is a fabric?
2 What are the two sorts of fibre?
3 Which fibres would be useful for a T-shirt or vest? Why?
4 Which fibres would be useful for waterproof leggings? Why?
5 What is the biggest disadvantage of wool? Explain your answer.
6 Plan an investigation to find the strength of a thread.

Keywords

fabric
thread
fibre
natural
artificial

12.2 Keeping it safe

How do we choose a fabric for a particular job?

Mountaineers need clothes that can cope with the toughest conditions. A waterproof and windproof jacket could save your life on a mountain. Different layers in the jacket do different jobs. Some jackets are made from a special 'breathing' fabric. This fabric keeps you warm and keeps water out but allows sweat to pass from your body to the outside.

Sometimes the way the cloth is made makes it expensive. The **weave** affects the way the fabric behaves when it is used. Tight weaves tend to be **waterproof** and **windproof**. Open weaves stretch easily and can trap air layers which help to keep people warm. Different **yarns** cost different amounts of money.

A student weighed a beaker with fabric fixed on the top.

She poured 10 ml of water slowly over the fabric. Some of the water went through into the beaker.

She weighed the beaker and the wet fabric. Then she repeated the experiment with four different fabrics.

Fabric	Dry fabric + beaker (g)	Wet fabric + beaker (g)	Weight of water (g)
Cotton	95	102	7
Waxed cotton	93	95	2
Nylon	90	94	4
Silicone nylon	98	99	1
Rubber	94	94	0

Questions

1 Draw a bar chart of the weight of water against the fabric.
2 Why do you think 10 ml of water was used for each fabric?
3 Which fabric is completely waterproof?
4 Which fabrics are only **water-resistant**?
5 Why do mountaineering jackets have more than one layer of fabric?

Keywords

weave

waterproof

windproof

yarn

water-resistant

12.3 Surliving fires

How can we make fabrics flameproof?

Firefighters depend on their clothes to save their lives. The fabrics reflect heat. They are treated with special chemicals so that they do not burn easily. Even so, fighting fires is a dangerous and difficult job.

All fabrics burn if they become hot enough. However, we can make it more difficult for them to catch fire. Some chemicals seem to reduce the chance of a fabric catching fire. We call fabrics that have been treated with these chemicals **flameproof**.

A student tested some fabrics to see how they burned before and after flameproofing. He used three equal pieces from each fabric and treated them with flameproofing chemicals.

He heated the fabrics with a bunsen burner. He timed how long before each fabric caught fire.

untreated

treated with **alum**

treated with **borax**

Fabric	Untreated (seconds)	Alum (seconds)	Borax (seconds)
Cotton	30	35	39
Nylon	23	30	36
Wool	25	32	37

Questions

1 List the ways in which firefighters' clothes protect them.

2 What does 'flameproof' mean?

3 Which fabric would be most suitable for making a flameproof coat? Why?

4 Which treatment would you use?

5 Firefighters' uniforms need to be washed regularly. How might this affect their flameproof coating?

6 Plan an investigation to check your answer to Question 3.

Keywords

flameproof

alum

borax

12.4 Bandages

Which bandage is best for a deep cut?

And it all started with a small cut on his finger! People have used fabrics for thousands of years to bind **wounds**. The **bandages** help to stop blood leaking out and dirt getting in.

Doctors and nurses have to use the right bandage for each job. Chemists develop new types of fabrics for wound dressings every year. The most modern ones let water pass out so that the cut does not get waterlogged. Some also help to kill microorganisms.

Properties of different sticking plasters

Sticking plastic	Supastrip	Reinforced Supastrip	Easystrip	Bare skin
How hard do you have to pull to break it?	★	★★★★	★★★★★	
How much water gets through per minute?	★★★★	★★★★	★★★	★★★★★
How many bacteria grow	★	★★	★★★★★	★★

A wound deeper than about 1.75 cm usually needs stitches. A doctor or nurse sews the two halves of the wound together with thread. Nowadays, glue or metal staples are used for skin wounds.

Stitching wounds

Thread	Notes
Cotton	Cheap. Does not dissolve so needs to be cut away when the wound has healed.
Cat gut	Dissolves – so does not need to be cut out when wound has healed. But can dissolve too quickly!
Superglue	No **stitches** to cut out. Often produces a neater wound that does not show. Less painful. Reduced risk of **infection**.
Staples	Easy to apply. Cause fewer infections. Easy to remove.

Questions

1 Which type of sticking plaster is the strongest?

2 Which type of sticking plaster lets most water through?

3 Give one disadvantage of Easystrip.

4 Give one disadvantage of cotton for stitches.

5 List three advantages of superglue for skin wounds.

6 Plan an investigation to find how sticky three different samples of sticking plaster are.

Keywords

wound

bandages

stitches

infection

12 Data response: Rock monkey

A climber's life could depend on their rope! If you slip it could mean the difference between life and death! Climbing ropes must be strong and also need a bit of 'give'. Imagine falling a long way and then being stopped by your rope. If it stops you too quickly the jolt could give you a nasty injury.

And ropes need to be light. Thicker ropes are stronger – but also heavier. Remember you have to carry this all the way up the mountain!

Table 1: *Properties of fibres used in climbing ropes*

Rope type	Weight (g/m)	Breaking strength (kg/mm)
Cotton	47	225
Hemp	63	300
Polyester fibre	39	784
Nylon fibre	42	616
Carbon fibre	85	3430
Steel	195	1330

Table 2: *Commercial ropes for climbing*

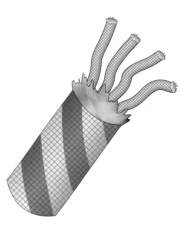

Rope	Diameter (mm)	Weight (g/m)	Number of falls before it must be thrown away	Breaking strength (kg)	Stretch (%)
Thin Double Happiness	8.5	48.2	8	602	7.6
Thick Double Happiness	9.0	53.3	12	630	7.0
Whippet	9.5	62.9	8	1018	5.8
Gym-Bo	10.8	77.8	9	1060	6.2
Glider	10.5	72	9	1120	6.6
Leavittator	11.0	75.2	14	962	4.8

Data response

1 Which fibre is the strongest?

2 Which are the two natural fibres in Table 1?

3 Draw a bar chart of the weight of the ropes in Table 1.

4 Steel is much stronger than everything except carbon fibre. Why is steel wire never used for climbing rope?

5 Table 2 shows the brand names of some ropes you can buy over the internet. Which rope would you buy for each of these people:
- I want the strongest possible rope.
- I want the lightest rope that has a breaking strength of over 900 kg.
- I want a stretchy rope.

6 How much would a 100 m roll of Whippet rope weigh?

Research

7 Plan an investigation to find out the breaking strength of a sample of cotton. You will need to find the lowest possible weight that will snap the thread. Once you have a method which works well, investigate one of these problems:
- Does a wet thread break more easily than a dry one?
- Does a thread that has been stretched break more easily than one that has not been stretched?

Presentation

8 Prepare a short article for radio, television or a magazine about choosing clothing for a walking expedition in Tibet. You will need to include details about the different types of fabrics used in the clothes and how the design of the clothes could keep you safe in cold and dangerous conditions.

Learning progress

I know:
- Some fibres are natural, for example cotton from cotton plants and wool from sheep. Other fibres are artificial (nylon, polythene and polyester) and are made by chemical reactions.
- Fibres can be twisted into threads to make ropes or woven into fabrics.
- Fibres and fabrics must be tested to find out their properties so that we can decide how they should be used.
- Waterproof fabrics are useful because they keep us dry. A disadvantage is that they do not let moisture from the body escape. This can make them uncomfortable to wear. Fabrics can be treated with chemicals to make them more waterproof. Fabrics like GoreTex keep water out but let moisture from the body pass out.
- Fabrics can be treated with chemicals to make them flameproof. These fabrics are used for people like firefighters or steel workers who work near flames.
- Fibres and fabrics used in medical situations must not harm the body. They often need to be chosen very carefully to match their properties to their uses.

I can:
- Make measurements to test a property of a fibre or fabric.
- Add results to a bar chart.

13.1 Carry on camping!

Which gases does air contain?

Fresh **air** – everyone loves a bit of it! Campers will sleep under canvas in the cold and wet just to get up to fresh air in the morning. No pollution or poisons: a perfect place!

The air around us is called the **atmosphere**. It contains a mixture of gases. When people say fresh air they usually mean air that has no pollutant gases or dust.

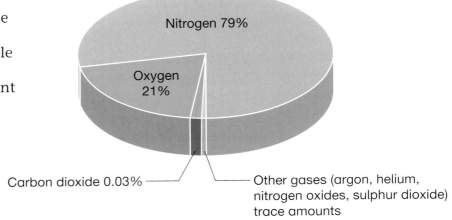

Nitrogen 79%

Oxygen 21%

Carbon dioxide 0.03% —

— Other gases (argon, helium, nitrogen oxides, sulphur dioxide) trace amounts

Questions

1 Which is the most common gas in the atmosphere?

2 Which gas takes up 21% of the air?

3 Which gas do animals need to survive?

4 Which substance in the table melts at the lowest temperature?

5 Which gas is becoming more common because of the burning of fossil fuels?

Keywords

air
atmosphere
nitrogen
oxygen
carbon dioxide

13.2 Traffic smells!

⇨ What pollution does traffic produce?

Cars produce a lot of **pollution**. The chemicals in the pollution are called **pollutants**. In some cities the air is so full of pollutants that it makes the people who live there ill. The bigger the car the worse the pollution it creates. The worst cars are the big all-terrain vehicles, essential in the city!

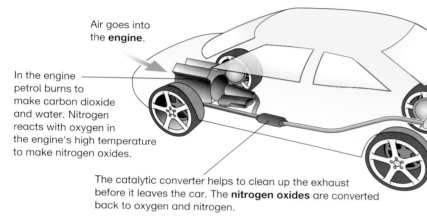

Air goes into the **engine**.

In the engine petrol burns to make carbon dioxide and water. Nitrogen reacts with oxygen in the engine's high temperature to make nitrogen oxides.

The catalytic converter helps to clean up the exhaust before it leaves the car. The **nitrogen oxides** are converted back to oxygen and nitrogen.

The exhaust pumps out tiny particles of soot, water vapour, carbon dioxide and nitrogen oxides.

The faster you drive the more pollution you produce. Slower, smaller cars do less damage but all cars produce some pollution.

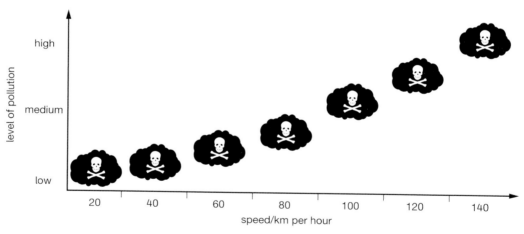

level of pollution

high

medium

low

20 40 60 80 100 120 140

speed/km per hour

Questions

1 What is a pollutant?

2 List three pollutants that come out of a car's exhaust.

3 Which sorts of cars produce the most pollution?

4 How can you reduce the amount of pollution a car produces?

5 Motorbikes produce less pollution than large cars. Why doesn't the government make cars illegal and force everyone to ride motorbikes instead?

Keywords

pollution

pollutant

engine

nitrogen oxides

13.3 The clean car?

Can we really build an environmentally friendly car?

There are millions of cars on Britain's roads. How can these be cleaned up so that they do not produce so much pollution? Motor manufacturers spend vast amounts of money each year trying to develop cleaner cars.

This **electric** car is clean, but it is not practical because it is too small for a family of four and their groceries. The best option would be a new kind of car called a **hybrid** that contains a **petrol** and an electric **engine** which try to cut pollution.

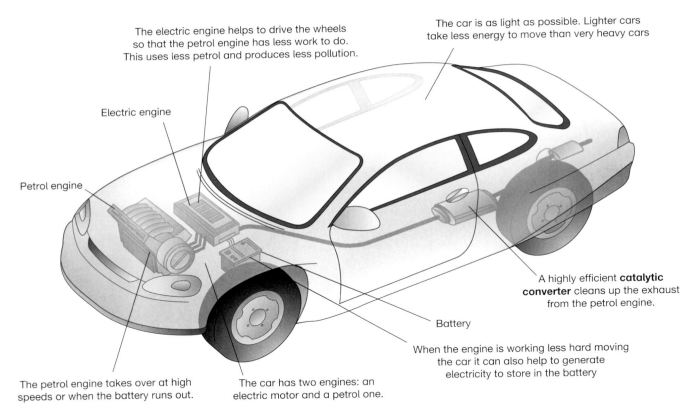

The electric engine helps to drive the wheels so that the petrol engine has less work to do. This uses less petrol and produces less pollution.

The car is as light as possible. Lighter cars take less energy to move than very heavy cars

Electric engine

Petrol engine

A highly efficient **catalytic converter** cleans up the exhaust from the petrol engine.

Battery

The petrol engine takes over at high speeds or when the battery runs out.

The car has two engines: an electric motor and a petrol one.

When the engine is working less hard moving the car it can also help to generate electricity to store in the battery

Questions

1 Why is an electric car cleaner than a petrol one?

2 Which engine starts the car in a hybrid vehicle?

3 What does a catalytic converter do?

4 Why are smaller cars often cleaner than large cars?

5 Where does the electricity for an electric car come from? How might this create pollution?

Keywords

electric

hybrid

petrol

engine

catalytic converter

clean air?

13.4   Dirty air

How bad is the air where you live? The map shows the **air pollution** across the UK. Where should you move to get clean air?

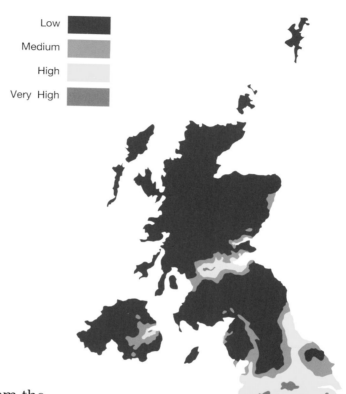

Low

Medium

High

Very High

Most of the wind in Britain comes from the west. The worst pollution is usually found on the eastern side of big cities. Why?

Clean air is needed in operating theatres. The theatres are pumped full of clean, sterile air at slightly higher than normal **pressure**. This means that the air leaks out of the theatre pushing out any dust and germs.

Rooms in factories making silicon chips for computers must be dust-free. Any dust can damage the delicate silicon chips before they are coated in plastic.

Questions

1   What is the level of sulphur dioxide in Bristol?

2   Is the air in Harlech cleaner than the air in Leeds?

3   List three gases measured at air pollution stations.

4   Why are silicon chips made in special dust-free rooms?

5   Why is the air pressure in operating theatres slightly higher than normal?

Keywords

air pollution

nitrogen oxides

pressure

13 Data response: Clean air

225,000 MakePovertyHistory campaigners marched around Edinburgh on July 2nd 2005. Traffic was kept out of the city centre and the air was measurably cleaner – despite all those people!

Traffic pumps millions of tonnes of tiny specks of carbon into the air every day. You can see these as black smoke coming out of the exhausts of cars, lorries and buses. Scientists can use machines to collect the particles from the air. The black specks stick to a length of sticky tape. The more specks of carbon the dirtier the air.

A 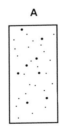 B  C  D  E

Data response

1 Which strip has the most particles?

2 Which strip comes from outside the city?

3 How can you tell which strip comes from outside the city?

4 What results would you expect if the tests were done on a day with a lot of traffic?

5 Draw a bar chart to show the results from all of the sample points.

Some samples have lost their labels.

6 Which sample is from position A?

7 Which sample is from position D?

8 There was no traffic in Edinburgh on the day of the march. Why were there still some carbon particles in the air?

Another important pollutant from traffic is acid gases. These dissolve in rain and water to make acid solutions.

9 Plan an investigation into the effects of acids on the growth of seeds. Use very dilute solutions of acids and small dishes to grow the seeds. Consider:
- how to measure how well the seeds grow
- how to make sure your test is fair
- what results to expect.

Presentation

10 Prepare an advertisement for a company that is selling hybrid electric cars. These cars produce less pollution. Your advert should show the advantages of this technology and briefly explain how the cars work. You can use text, pictures and even sound and video if you can get hold of a computer. Your advert could be for television, radio, a magazine or even a poster.

Learning progress

I know:

- The Earth is surrounded by air in the atmosphere. Air contains about 80 per cent nitrogen and 20 per cent oxygen and smaller amounts of water vapour, carbon dioxide and other gases.

- Fuels contain carbon, which turns to carbon dioxide when they burn. Limewater turns milky white when carbon dioxide bubbles through it.

- Burning fuels adds harmful chemicals to the atmosphere. These are called pollutants because they are harmful to humans or the environment.

- Nitrogen and oxygen in the air react together to make nitrogen oxides in a car engine. Nitrogen oxides can cause breathing problems and acid rain. Carbon particles (soot and smoke) can damage the lungs.

- Catalytic converters in cars reduce pollutants like nitrogen oxides by converting them back to nitrogen and oxygen.

- Clean, unpolluted air is essential in operating theatres and 'clean rooms' used to build silicon chips for computers and other electronic equipment.

I can:

- Use the internet to find out information about air pollution and display this on a chart.

- Carry out a test to show the presence of carbon dioxide.

Respond • Research • Present

14.1 On your bike!

 What is the best material for a mountain bike?

So, metal or plastic? In the past that would have been an easy question to answer. Metals were the strongest, lightest **materials** to make mountain bikes. Nowadays new materials developed by chemistry are as strong as metals and often lighter and cheaper to make. Will next year's mountain bike be cheaper, stronger and lighter than last year's?

Alloys are mixtures of two or more metals. The properties of an alloy may be very different to the properties of the pure metals it contains.

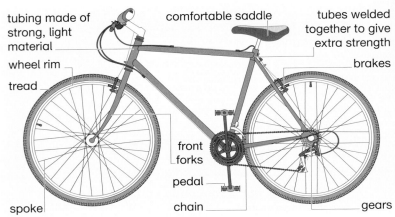

tubing made of strong, light material
comfortable saddle
tubes welded together to give extra strength
wheel rim
brakes
tread
front forks
pedal
spoke
chain
gears

Metal or alloy	Density/g cm^3	Strength (1 = weakest)	Does it rust?
Pure iron	7. 9	4	Yes
Pure aluminium	2.7	1	No
Aluminium alloy	2.8	8	No
Steel alloy	7.8	6	Yes
Chromaloy	7.9	9	No
Plastic	3.4	5	No
Carbon fibre composite	2.8	12	No

Questions

1 Which of the materials has the lowest **density**?

2 Which of the materials is the strongest?

3 Aluminium alloy bike frames need much thicker tubing than chromaloy ones. Why?

4 Steel frames have to be painted but aluminium alloy frames do not. Why?

5 Why are all bikes not made of carbon fibre?

6 Draw a bar chart to show the density of the materials in the table.

Keywords

material

alloy

density

Strong stuff

14.2 Joining up

 How can we stick parts together?

Metal structures usually contain more than one part. To join these parts together the builders can use bolts or they can **solder** or **weld** the metal pieces. The Eden Project domes uses thousands of special bolts to hold the giant hexagons together. Engineers could not weld the hexagons together because the plastic filling them would melt.

Electricians often use a solder to join metal wires to a circuit board. A solder is an alloy of **lead** and **tin** that melts at a low temperature.

Welding	Soldering	Bolts
Parts get very hot	Parts get hot	Parts do not get hot
The metals melt together	The solder melts to hold the metals	The nut and bolt hold the parts together
Very strong joint	Weak joint	Joint is as strong as the bolt
Needs heavy welding equipment	Needs a small electric tool	Needs a spanner

In a welded joint the two metals are heated until they melt together.

In a soldered joint the metals do not melt. They are held together by the solder when it goes solid.

Questions

1 List four ways to join metal parts together.
2 Builders did not weld the Eden Project dome frames together. Why?
3 What is an alloy?
4 Name the two metals used to make a solder.
5 Why are joints on circuit boards soldered not welded?
6 Plan an investigation to test the strength of a new kind of glue for wood.

Keywords

solder

weld

lead

tin

14.3 Filling a gap!

 What are dental fillings made from?

Teeth are made of the hardest substance in the human body. It is called **enamel**. If you look after your teeth they will last a lifetime. But too many sugary foods lead to decay. Dentists drill out the decayed part of the tooth and fill the gap with an **alloy**. Sometimes the complete tooth needs to be replaced. Dentists use special plastics or even gold to do this.

Dentists usually use an alloy containing **mercury** to fill teeth. Alloys containing mercury are called **amalgams**. The dentist's assistant mixes silver, copper and other metals with mercury to make a paste. The dentist fills the hole in the tooth with the paste and waits for it to set hard.

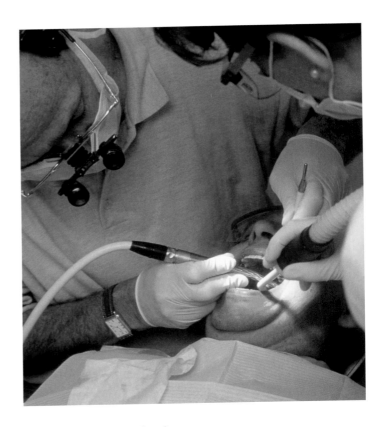

Some new fillings use materials called **composites**. A composite is a material that contains two or more different substances. The composite used for fillings contains silica powder and a resin. The resin acts like a glue and sets to make a tough filling.

Mercury amalgam	Silica-resin composite
Silver-grey colour	Can be matched to the colour of the tooth
Contains mercury which is harmful	Contains no mercury
Can produce allergies	No known allergies
Filling has to be wedged into the hole	Filling is bonded to the remains of the tooth
Can be used for filling large holes in back teeth	No good for large holes in back teeth
Quick to do	Slower to do
Cheaper than composite materials	More expensive than mercury amalgam

Questions

1 What name is given to a mixture of metals containing mercury?
2 Write down three advantages of composite materials for filling teeth.
3 Write down three disadvantages of composite materials for filling teeth.
4 Plan a test to find out how easily a material for filling teeth can be broken. If you can, carry out your test on samples of plaster or concrete.
5 Plan an investigation to find out the strength of four different plastics.

Keywords

enamel
alloy
mercury
amalgam
composite

to come text to come

Clay is soft and water turns it to liquid. Not the best building material! But heat clay to high temperatures and you end up with a hard substance that resists water. The Vertical Stack Brick Kiln uses local clay to make cheap bricks for homes in India.

A mixture of local clay is used to make the bricks.

Cutting the clay into the correct shape.

*The brick **kiln** – the platform lets people wheel bricks on trolleys to the top of the kiln.*

*Bricks are loaded into the top with lumps of charcoal. The **charcoal** burns at a very high temperature to fire the clay. It also gives out very little smoke so it is much healthier for the workers and produces much less **pollution** than older methods.*

A platform lets the bricks pass through the kiln. Steel rods hold the stack of bricks in place. The giant wheel turns to control the position of the bricks in the kiln.

Bricks are removed at the bottom. the kiln can carry on working at the top while the bricks are removed from the bottom.

A perfect brick for house building!

But a wall is more than just bricks. The **mortar** that holds it together is made from sand and cement mixed with water. As the cement sets it changes from a wet, sloppy mixture to a hard mix that holds the bricks in place.

Questions

1 List two differences between clay and finished bricks before and after firing.

2 Why are bricks easier to build with than stones?

3 Give two advantages of the vertical kiln compared with older methods.

4 What does mortar contain?

6 Plan an investigation to find out the strength of a VSBK brick.

Keywords

clay

kiln

charcoal

pollution

mortar

14 Data response: It's a racket

Tennis players can now hit a ball so hard it travels at over 100 mph! Get in the way of one of those serves and you could get something worse than a black eye! The top speed of a tennis serve has been going up over the last few years. Is this because the players are getting stronger or is it something to do with the tennis rackets?

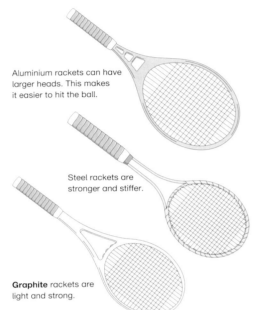

Aluminium rackets can have larger heads. This makes it easier to hit the ball.

Steel rackets are stronger and stiffer.

Graphite rackets are light and strong.

Material	Density/ g cm³	Strength (1 = weakest)	Does it rust?
Wood	0.7	3	No
Aluminium alloy	2.8	8	No
Steel	7.8	6	Yes
Graphite	1.9	15	No
Rubber	0.9	0.2	No
Polythene	0.9	0.1	No

Speed of first serves

Player	No. of serves	Avg MPH
Marcelo Rios	2	92 mph
Jim Courie	6	108 mph
Todd Martin	7	98 mph
Tomas Muster	8	105 mph
Pete Sampras	11	120 mph
Petr Korda	7	101 mph
Andre Agassi	9	102 mph
Mark Philippousis	3	123 mph
Michael Chang	7	112 mph
Tim Henman	2	120 mph

Speed of second serves

Player	No. of serves	Avg MPH
Andre Agassi	9	74 mph
Tim Henman	2	85 mph
Pete Sampras	4	85 mph
Tomas Muster	2	71 mph
Mark Philippousis	4	99 mph
Petr Korda	3	88 mph
Michael Chang	10	77 mph
Jim Courier	4	91 mph
Todd Martin	10	89 mph

All data from the 1997 US Open

Data response

1 Which material is the strongest?

2 Give two advantages of graphite over steel for making a tennis racket.

3 Draw a bar chart to show the differences in strength of the materials in the table.

4 Steel is twice as strong as wood so why is it not used for tennis rackets?

5 Who was the fastest server at the 1997 US Open?

6   Why is the data for Pete Sampras more reliable than the data for Tim Henman?

7   What is the average difference in speed between first and second serves?

Research

Tight strings give a firmer surface to hit against the ball. Does this give a stronger serve? Plan an investigation to find out how the surface on which a ball bounces affects the height of the bounce.

You will need to use the same ball for each test. Why is this a problem? (Clue: Think about what happens when the umpire at tennis match calls for 'new balls')

Presentation

Sports equipment companies are always bringing out new versions of racquets, bats and so on. They often claim that the new kit will 'improve your game'.

Prepare a presentation for a new piece of kit. You can choose any sport (tennis, cricket, snowboarding etc.). Your presentation must show how new materials make this new piece of equipment better than the old one.

Learning progress

I know:

- Metals are good conductors of heat and electricity and are strong shiny. Non-metals are not.

- An alloy is a mixture of two or more elements, at least one of which is a metal. Steel is an alloy used to make bridges, cars and buildings. Solder is used to join electrical compounds together. Aluminium alloys are used in plans and other structures which need to be light and strong. Brass is a decorative alloy. The properties of alloys are different from the properties of themetals from which they are made.

- Hard minerals are used for making jewellery and buildings. Bricks are made from clay. They need to be fired in a kiln before they are used. Mortar is made from sand and cement. It holds bricks in place. Concrete is made from cement, sand and small stones. It is used for strong structures.

- Tennis rackets can be made from carbon fibre, metals and wooden frames. Each material has different advantages. Carbon fibre is light and strong. Metals are strong. Wood is light and cheap.

- Glass reinforced plastic is used for sports equipment like canoes. Reinforced concrete is used in buildings. Plywood is used to make furniture and in buildings.

I can:

- Identify iron and steel using a magnet, copper aluminium and lead by sight.
- Make a sample of concrete and test it for strength.

15.1 Codes

 Why do we all need codes?

message → encode → secret code → decode → message

Every spy needs a secret **code**! Information is **encoded** and sent to the secret contact. The contact **decodes** the message to get to the original information. But even ordinary people want some secret codes. If you buy something on the internet, deal with an online bank or send music files, you want to be secure.

One of the first codes used to send messages was **Morse** code. It used dots and dashes to represent letters of the alphabet. These small signals were sent down wires and made a tapping noise at the receiving end. The operator decoded these taps to make the original message. Not an easy job!

The wires and switches used to send the message were not perfect. They added crackles and hiss to the **signal**. These are called **noise**. The coded information is called the signal. If the noise is louder than the signal the message is drowned out. All message systems add some noise to the signal. The less noise added the better. The further the message has to be sent the more noise the system adds. This is why phone calls to other countries can be more crackly than a call to your next door neighbour.

Questions

1 Write a sentence including the words 'code' and 'decode'.

2 List three situations where a code must be secret to work properly.

3 What is the name of the code that uses dots and dashes to represent letters of the alphabet?

4 What is noise?

5 List three ways in which a coded message can go wrong.

Keywords

code

encode

decode

Morse

signal

noise

Digital age

15.2 Digital music

How do iPods work?

Everyone's got an iPod these days! Even monks in Tibet can get their share of music! Any iPod holds many hours of music – held in a code called MP3 or MP4. A tiny computer in the iPod recreates the music from the code and sends it to the headphones. The code is a very good way to store music – you can pack a lot of music into a small space.

An iPod is a **digital** device. If you add random **noise** to a digital **signal** special filters can remove it and leave a clean signal. Signals used on vinyl records or old-fashioned telephones were **analogue**. Analogue signals look like waves. If you add noise to these the wave is destroyed – there is no way to get back to the original.

music → code → MP4 → decode → music

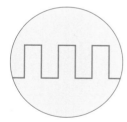

clean digital signal

clean analogue signal

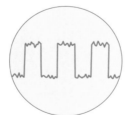

noisy digital signal

noisy analogue signal

Questions

1 What is the code the iPod uses to store so much music?

2 Draw a picture of a clean digital signal.

3 Draw a picture of a clean analogue signal.

4 Why do digital signals give clearer sound than analogue ones?

5 The monk's iPod holds 40 gigabytes. One gigabyte is a thousand megabytes. MP4 uses one megabyte for every minute of music. How many minutes of music will fit on the iPod?

Keywords

digital

noise

signal

analogue

15.3 I'm on my mobile!

How do mobile phones work?

It's not just iPods in Tibet – everyone's got a **mobile** phone as well! This guy is probably just texting his mates at the monastery!

Modern mobile phones use **digital signals** to give clear sound – and pictures, and texts and even video! Satellites above the Earth and masts attached to buildings make sure you can get a signal almost everywhere. So mobiles are perfect? Not quite.

Mobile phones give out **microwave radiation** when they are used. Some scientists worry that this radiation may cause some sorts of brain cancers. The evidence is not conclusive but they suggest people should try to:

- Limit the use of mobile phones

- Use a handfree kit to keep the phone away from your ear (which is right next to your brain!)

- Use texts not voice messages

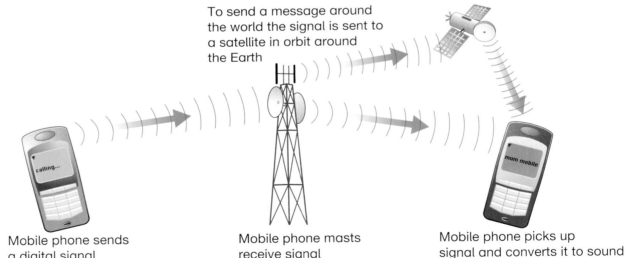

To send a message around the world the signal is sent to a satellite in orbit around the Earth

Mobile phone sends a digital signal

Mobile phone masts receive signal

Mobile phone picks up signal and converts it to sound

Questions

1 Modern mobile phones use a digital signal. Why?

2 What receives the signal when you call someone with a mobile?

3 Why do some people not want mobile phone masts near their homes?

4 Give three ways you can reduce the risk of using a mobile phone.

5 Why are satellites needed for some phone messages?

Keywords

mobile
digital
signal
microwave
radiation

15.4 Wireless communications

 What are the advantages of wireless communications?

Every home has at least three of them – but trying to find them is a nightmare! Why are **remote** controls so popular?

Almost all remote controls use **infrared** signals. These travel short distances and are safer than the microwave radiation used by mobile phones.

Devices	Type of connection	Reason for using it
Computers	**Bluetooth**	To attach keyboard and mice – means you do not have to carry cables with you everywhere.
Computer	**WiFi**	To connect to networks without the need for wires.
Televisions and video recorders	Infrared	So that you don't need to get out of your chair when you're watching television!
Stereos	Infrared	You can balance the sound perfectly from the place where you are listening to the music.

System	Advantages	Disadvantages
Bluetooth	Secure Very small transmitters and receivers	Relatively expensive Cannot work over long distances Carries small amounts of information
Infrared	Cheap	Cannot work over long distances
WiFi	Carries a lot of information Can work up to distances of up to 100 metres	Expensive Needs quite a large transmitter and receiver

Questions

1 What is the main advantage of infrared wireless connections?

2 What is the main disadvantage of wifi connections?

3 Computers do not use Bluetooth to connect to the internet. Why?

4 Give two advantages of a mobile phone with Bluetooth.

5 Many airports have a wifi connection nowadays. Why do they do this?

Keywords

remote

infrared

Bluetooth

WiFi

15 Data response: Coded messages

Morse code alphabet

A	.−
B	−...
C	−.−.
D	−..
E	.
F	..−.
G	−−.
H	....
I	..
J	.−−−
K	−.−
L	.−..
M	−−
N	−.
O	−−−
P	.−−.
Q	−−.−
R	.−.
S	...
T	−
U	..−
V	...−
W	.−−
X	−..−
Y	−.−−
Z	−−..
0	−−−−−
1	.−−−−
2	..−−−
3	...−−
4	....−
5	.....
6	−....
7	−−...
8	−−−..
9	−−−−.
Fullstop	.−.−.−
Comma	−−..−−
Query	..−−..

1791   Samuel Morse born.

1840   Morse code invented.

1844   First coded message sent by telegraph: 'What hath God wrought?'

1852   A cable is laid under the English Channel. Paris and London now connected by telegraph.

1858   The first transatlantic message is sent from Queen Victoria to the US President. The cable stops working one month after it was laid.

1866   The first reliable transatlantic cable is completed.

1872   Morse dies in New York.

1880   Roughly 100,000 miles of undersea cable have been laid.

···/⁻·⁻·/··/·/⁻·/⁻·⁻·/·/··/···/··⁻·/··⁻/⁻·

Data response

1 When was Samuel Morse born?
2 Who sent the first transatlantic telegraph message?
3 Write this message as morse code: 'Science Plus is great'.
4 What does the mystery message above say?
5 Give one advantage of morse code.
6 Give one disadvantage of morse code.

Research

7 Are mobile phones safe? Carry out a search on the web to find out. Try to find evidence on both sides of the question.

Presentation

8 Secret codes are essential for things like internet banking and online shopping. Prepare a poster to explain why sharing your password with someone else is dangerous.

Learning progress

I know:

- Coding a message increases its security. Errors can happen when messages are sent. Noise carries no useful information and can cause errors. Noise increases as the signal travels further and limits the range of a message transfer system.

- Morse code uses a code of short dots and longer dashes. Analogue signals have a continuously variable value and digital signals are either on or off. MP3 players use digital signals.

- The signals used in mobile phones may be dangerous. They might increase the risk of some sorts of brain cancer. Using a phone less often, keeping it away from your ear and using texts instead of voice messages can reduce this risk.

- Mobile phone masts give out more radiation than phones. Masts should not be sited too near people.

- Remote controls in the home usually use infrared radiation. This is safer than the radiation used by mobile phones. Wireless communication devices use radio signals.

I can:

- Send and receive a message in Morse code.

16.1 Batteries

How do batteries make electricity?

Batteries come in different shapes and sizes. Some are rechargeable and others must be thrown away when they wear out. Different types of batteries are used for different jobs. Many electric cars use giant batteries that weigh more than their engines!

Camera: needs a little energy to drive the electronic circuits and flash.

Every battery has two **terminals**, each of which is a different metal. Inside the battery there is a liquid or paste between the terminals. This is called the **electrolyte**. Some solutions can conduct electricity. **Chemical reactions** inside the battery make **electricity** flow along a wire connected to the terminals. This electricity is used to power all sorts of electrical devices.

Drill: uses a lot of energy while it is working.

Torch: good batteries will last about 12 hours in this torch.

Batteries usually have the **voltage** written on them. You wouldn't be able to drive an electric car with a battery of the same voltage as the one you use in your personal stereo! You can use a voltmeter to check the voltage of a battery.

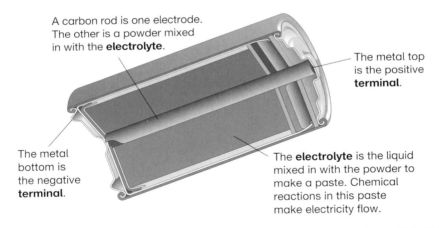

A carbon rod is one electrode. The other is a powder mixed in with the **electrolyte**.

The metal top is the positive **terminal**.

The metal bottom is the negative **terminal**.

The **electrolyte** is the liquid mixed in with the powder to make a paste. Chemical reactions in this paste make electricity flow.

Car: the electricity is needed to start the engine running and make the petrol burn.

Questions

1 What is a battery?

2 Name three things at home that own that contain batteries.

3 How would you find out the voltage of a battery that was not labelled?

4 Why do different battery-operated devices need batteries of different voltages?

5 We already have electric cars. Why are electric planes much harder to build?

Keywords

battery

terminal

electrolyte

chemical reactions

electricity

voltage

Power on!

16.2 Power stations

 How do power stations make electricity?

Power stations make electricity. How do they do this? To make electricity just move a **magnet** near a wire. The movement makes electricity flow along the wire. A **generator** is a machine that produces electricity. They usually have a magnet spinning around inside a **coil** – or a coil spinning around in a magnet!

You can increase the amount of electricity produced by:

- using a more powerful magnet
- wrapping the wire into a coil with lots of turns
- spinning the magnet more quickly.

But how can you move the wire? Or the magnet? You need a source of **energy**. Most power stations use fossil fuels like gas, coal or oil to boil water. The steam is forced through a turbine and makes it turn at high speed. The turbine turns the generator to make electricity. Unfortunately, power stations waste energy at every stage in the process and many produce large amounts of waste heat and carbon dioxide.

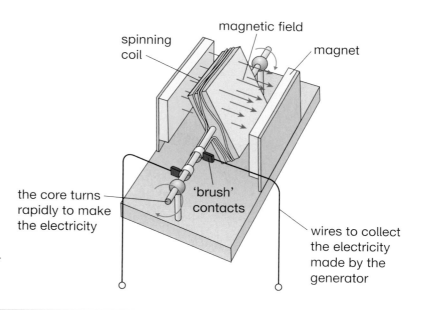

spinning coil · magnetic field · magnet · the core turns rapidly to make the electricity · 'brush' contacts · wires to collect the electricity made by the generator

Questions

1 What does a generator do?
2 What three things do you need to generate electricity?
3 List three ways to increase the amount of electricity made by a generator.
4 Suggest four sources of energy to turn the magnet in a generator.
5 A dynamo is a tiny generator that produces electricity to light the bulb on a bicycle. Where does the energy to turn the generator come from?

Keywords

magnet
generator
coil
energy

16.3 The national grid

How do transformers help electricity get to our home?

The **mains** electricity in your home is 240 volts – enough to give you a very nasty shock! The voltage for your mobile phone might be 3.6 V – too small for you even to feel if you touched the contacts in the battery. A laptop computer might need power at 24 V. To convert electricity between these different voltages you need a **transformer**.

A transformer contains two **coils** of wire wrapped around a large **core** of iron. One coil is the **input** – you put electricity into this coil. The other coil is the **output** – electricity comes out of this coil. The number of turns in each coil controls the voltage of the electricity that comes out.

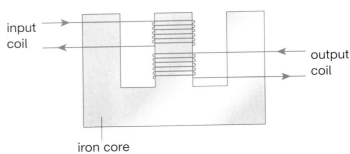

iron core

Power on!

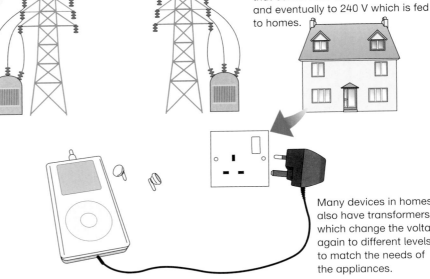

Electricity in the national grid is at 400,000 volts! This makes it easier to move power around. Devices called transformers convert electricity from the power station to this high voltage.

Electricity substations have transformers that convert the 400 kV to lower voltages and eventually to 240 V which is fed to homes.

Power stations make large amounts of electricity. This needs to be carried to homes and factories where it will be used. The national grid does this job.

Many devices in homes also have transformers which change the voltage again to different levels to match the needs of the appliances.

Questions

1 What is the voltage of the mains electricity at home?

2 What is a typical voltage for a small mobile phone?

3 How many transformers do you have at home?

4 What does a transformer do?

5 Why do you sometimes need different transformers to use electrical equipment in different countries?

Keywords

mains

transformer

coil

core

input

output

16.4 Paying the bills

How can you work out your electricity bill?

Electricity costs money. The more you use, the more you pay. An electricity meter records how much electricity has been used. The meter lets the electricity company work out how much to charge the customer.

Electricity is sold in **units**. One unit of electricity is enough to:
- listen to your stereo for ten hours, or
- watch television for eight hours, or
- run a single bar electric fire for one hour.

Appliances that give out heat tend to use a lot of electricity. We can work out how much electricity something uses by looking at its **power** rating. Powerful appliances use a lot of electricity. Power is measured in watts (using the symbol W). A thousand watts used every hour is called a **kilowatt-hour** (kWh) or one unit of electricity.

To calculate an electricity bill:

NATIONAL ELECTRIC

Present meter reading	30568
Previous meter reading	30155
Units used	413
Price per unit	8p
Cost of electricity used	£33.04
Add a charge for the meter	£12.50
Total to pay	**£45.54**

Take this number from the one above

Multiply the cost by the number

Convert your answer to pounds

Add the two numbers above to find the total

Questions

1 What is electrical power measured in?

2 Look at the electricity bill above. How many units of electricity have been used?

3 How much does each unit cost?

4 How much is the bill in total?

5 If the electricity company increased the cost of a unit by 2p, what would the new bill be?

Keywords

electricity

unit

power

kilowatt-hour

16 Data response: A cheaper supply?

Fancy having this parked in your back garden to provide electricity?

	Cost to set up (£)	Cost per unit in first year (£)	Increase in cost every year (£)
Mains electricity	20	8	+1
Solar panels	2000	0	0
Wind power	1750	0	0

Data response

1. How much does it cost to set up a windmill for a house?
2. How much does each unit of electricity cost from the mains in year 1?
3. How much does each unit of electricity cost from the mains in year 5?
4. A household uses 3500 units of electricity every year. How much would it cost in the first year if they used mains electricity?

Power on!

5 How much would it cost to buy 3500 units from the mains in year 3?

6 What is the total cost for five years electricity from:
- mains electricity?
- solar panels?
- a windmill?

Research

7 Plan an investigation to find out how much electricity a solar panel produces in bright light and in dim light.

Presentation

8 Prepare a television advert for a house that gets all of its electricity from solar panels on the roof. Create a storyboard for the 30 second advert. If you get the chance use a video camera and computer to make the actual advert.

Learning progress

I know:

- Some solutions will conduct electricity. Electricity is made by chemical reactions in a battery. Two different metals are needed for the terminals of a battery. Different situations need different sorts of batteries.

- We pay for electricity by the unit. Some appliances use more electricity than others. Electricity meters count the units of electricity used in a building. The electricity bill multiplies the units used by the cost per unit and adds a standing charge to get the final amount to pay.

- Every power station needs an energy source. Crude oil, coal and natural gas are fossil fuels used in power stations.

- The main stages in the production of electricity are: using heat from an energy source to boil water to make steam, the steam turns turbines which turn a generator which makes electricity. Energy is wasted at each of these stages.

- Electricity is transferred from a power station through a grid of high voltage transmission lines. Transformers are used at the ends of the transmission lines to increase or decrease the voltage. This means less energy is wasted in the power lines.

- A transformer has two coils of wire wound onto a core of iron. Transformers can change the voltage of energy.

I can:

- Use a voltmeter to measure the voltage of a simple battery.
- Use a domestic electricity meter to find the cost of using electricity.

17.1 Magnets

 Are all metals magnetic?

This body scanner uses giant magnets to take pictures of the inside of your body. Powerful computers interpret the readings to make a kind of three-dimensional X-ray.

Magnets are made of iron or steel. Things which stick to magnets are called **magnetic**. Only three pure metals are magnetic: **iron**, **nickel** and **cobalt**. Steel is magnetic because it contains iron. The magnetic tape in cassettes contains tiny bits of iron stuck in a plastic ribbon.

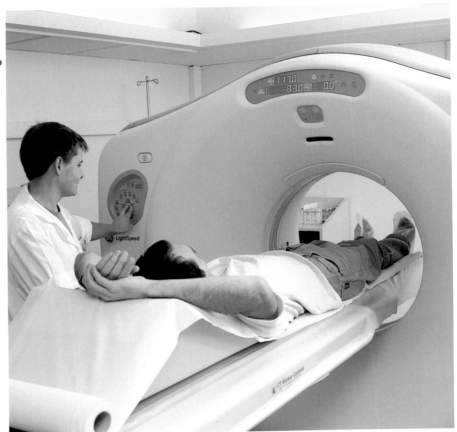

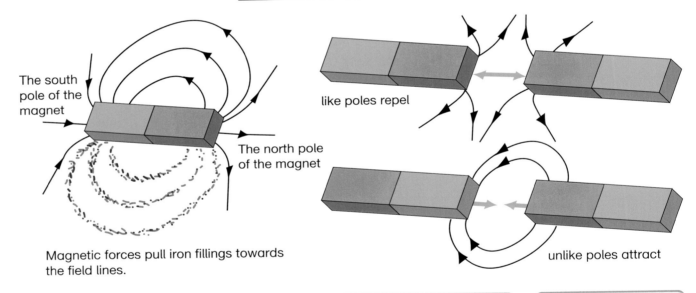

The south pole of the magnet

The north pole of the magnet

Magnetic forces pull iron fillings towards the field lines.

like poles repel

unlike poles attract

Feel the force

Questions

1 How many magnetic materials are there in your classroom?

2 What are the two poles of a magnet called?

3 If you put the north poles of two magnets together, what happens?

4 What happens when you put the north pole of one magnet next to the south pole of another magnet?

5 Why should you keep powerful magnets away from video cassettes?

Keywords

magnet

magnetic

iron

nickel

cobalt

17.2 Finding your way

 How does a compass work?

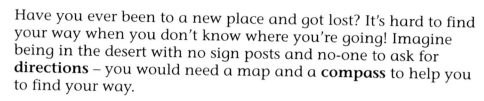

Have you ever been to a new place and got lost? It's hard to find your way when you don't know where you're going! Imagine being in the desert with no sign posts and no-one to ask for **directions** – you would need a map and a **compass** to help you to find your way.

The Earth acts as a giant magnet. It has a **magnetic field** around it that makes magnets point North-South. This is why a compass needle always points in the correct direction. The magnetic field also protects us against radiation from space called cosmic rays. You can see these near the poles as bright lights in the sky called the Northern lights.

Questions

1 Which of the Earth's poles does the red end of the compass needle point towards?

2 Find out whether you live in the north, south, east or west of your town or village.

3 Which direction is your school from your house?

4 Why are compass needles made of steel rather than plastic?

5 Your plastic compass is broken and you are miles from home on the hills. You still have the needle. Suggest two ways you could use the needle to find which way was north.

Keywords

direction

compass

magnetic field

17.3 Magnets and electricity

➡️ How do you make an electromagnet?

A steel pin can be **magnetised** by stroking it with a permanent magnet. But this is not the best way – it's better to use electricity. If you wrap a **coil** of wire around a steel bar and pass electricity through the wire the bar becomes magnetic. This is called an **electromagnet** and some electromagnets can be very strong.

This train hovers just above the ground – held in place by powerful electromagnets. To make a more powerful electromagnet you can:

- Increase the number of **turns** in the coil of wire
- Increase the amount of electricity flowing.

Electromagnets are very useful because when you switch off the electricity the magnetism disappears. This means you can turn the magnet on and off to pick up things like scrap metal.

Electricity flowing in any wire creates some magnetism. The powerlines that carry electricity for the national grid create magnetic fields around them. Some scientists are concerned that these magnetic fields might be dangerous. A survey of 30,000 children who had developed cancer between 1962 and 1995 found some frightening results. The risk of contracting **leukaemia** is still very small and more research is being done now to check these results.

A power pack supplies the electromagnet with electricity. When the electricity is on, a **magnetic field** forms. The nail and **coil** behave like a bar magnet.

This meter shows how much electric current you are using.

Distance from powerlines and leukaemia risk:

Distance from powerline	Relative risk of leukaemia for children born near the cables
Less than 200 m	1.69
Between 200 and 600 m	1.23
More than 600 m from cables	1.00

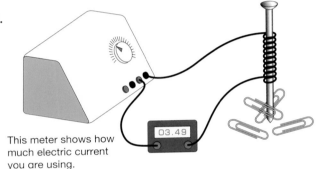

Questions

1. List two ways to magnetise a steel bar.
2. Give two advantages of electromagnets compared with ordinary magnets.
3. List three devices that use electromagnets.
4. How can you increase the strength of an electromagnet?
5. Powerlines can cause some types of cancer. Explain how the data in Table 1 supports this idea.

Keywords

magnetised

coil

electromagnet

turn

leukaemia

17.4 Make some noise

How do loudspeakers work?

Live8 was a huge concert in Hyde Park in London. Nearly 250,000 fans came to enjoy the music and learn about global trade justice. Giant speakers are used to make sure that every one of the tens of thousands of spectators can hear the music. The speakers are in large towers on either side of the stage.

Loudspeakers use **electromagnets** to work. The electromagnet makes a **cone** of paper vibrate, which produces **sounds** in the air.

The music player sends electrical signals to the **coil**. Signals switch the electromagnet on and off. The large permanent **magnet** helps to push and pull on the small coil.

large permanent magnet

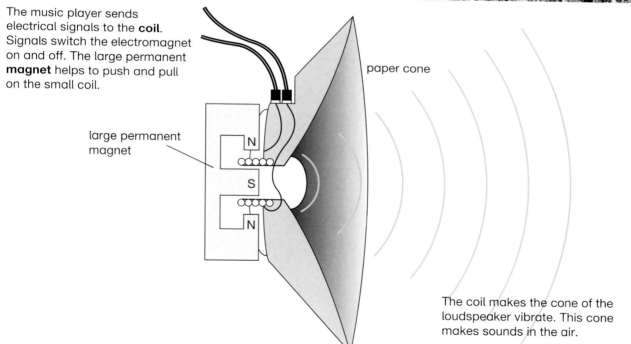

paper cone

The coil makes the cone of the loudspeaker vibrate. This cone makes sounds in the air.

Questions

1 List five things that use a loudspeaker.
2 How does the electrical signal get into the loudspeaker?
3 Which bit of the loudspeaker makes the sound?
4 What happens to the cone when the coil becomes a magnet?
5 What happens to the coil when the signal reaches the speaker?

Keywords

electromagnet

cone

sound

coil

magnet

17 Data response: Comparing headphones

A good selection of speakers to choose from! Most of the boxes, called cabinets, contain more than one speaker. The large speakers are good for low sounds. The smaller ones, called tweeters, are good for high-pitched notes. Fabric covers clip onto the front of the cabinet to hide the speakers when you use them.

Speaker Brand	Model	Colour	Cabinet (H × W × D) (cms)	Power rating (Watts)	Price per pair (£)	Number of speakers per cabinet
Morland Shout	Solo	Black	35 × 15 × 15	30	50	1
	Trio I	Silver	35 × 15 × 15	70	95	3
	Trio II	Silver	35 × 15 × 15	100	125	3
	Trio III	Silver	35 × 15 × 15	150	175	3
Bestman	Nottingham	Beech	30 × 15 × 15	25	45	1
	Leeds	Beech	50 × 20 × 20	50	40	3
	Manchester	Beech	70 × 30 × 25	75	130	3
Transmission	Studio	Silver or black	70 × 30 × 35	75	150	3
	Studio Monitor	Silver or black	95 × 35 × 50	150	219	3
	Studio Monitor +	Silver or black	95 × 35 × 50	165	259	3
	Reference	Black	105 × 45 × 70	200	349	5
	Reference XL	Black	105 × 45 × 70	225	399	5

Data response

1 Which is the cheapest set of speakers?

2 Which is the most expensive set of speakers made by Bestman?

3 Which two sorts of speakers can handle more than 175 W?

4 I have a shelf that is 40 cm high. Which speaker that can handle 50 W will fit on my shelf?

5 Which speaker has more than three different speakers built into each cabinet?

6 The tweeter works very well for particular sorts of sounds. What are these?

7 I have £100 to spend. What is the most powerful set of speakers I can afford?

Research

8 Build an electromagnet and test it. Try to produce the strongest possible electromagnet by answering some of the following questions:
- How does the number of turns in the coil affect the strength of the electromagnet?
- Is an electromagnet with a metal core stronger? Does the core have to be metal? What sort of metal works best?
- Does a wide coil work better than a narrow one? How does the length of the coil affect the strength of the magnet?

Presentation

9 Prepare a presentation about magnets for a local primary school. You should suggest some fun things for the pupils to do with magnets and make sure they understand the following:
- North and South poles
- Like poles repel, unlike poles attract
- A compass contains a magnet.

Make sure your presentation is exciting!

Learning progress

I know:
- Iron and steel are magnetic. Magnets attract magnetic materials. Like poles on a magnet repel and unlike poles attract. Iron filings or a compass can show a magnetic field. A freely swinging magnet comes to rest in a North-South direction. This is how a compass works. The red end of the magnetic needle always points North.
- You can induce magnetism in a pin by bringing a permanent magnet near it or by wrapping it in a wire carrying an electric current.
- A wire carrying a current behaves like a magnet.
- A loudspeaker contains a powerful electromagnet, an iron core and a paper or plastic cone. The electric signal changes the magnetic field in the loudspeaker. This makes the cone vibrate to make the sound we can hear.

I can:
- Use a compass to find the direction of a magnetic field.
- Use a plotting compass to map the magnetic field around a coil.

18.1 It is rocket science

How can we escape from Earth's gravity?

One of the most exciting journeys of all time began in Cape Kennedy, Florida, just after 9.30 am on July 16th 1969. Three men started their journey to the Moon. The journey finished in the Sea of Tranquillity at nearly 5.00 pm on 24th July.

Buzz Aldrin on the Moon in 1969.

Command module 3 m

Service module 7 m

Lunar module 7 m

3rd stage 18 m

2nd stage 25 m

1st stage 42 m

The third stage rocket fires to push the astronauts towards the Moon.

The command module splashes down in the ocean.

The **lunar module** lands on the Moon.

Most of the rocket is used to push the third stage into **orbit**. When the fuel has been used up the empty rocket falls back to Earth. It burns up in the atmosphere.

The command and service modules return to Earth.

Questions

1 Which part of the rocket landed on the Moon?

2 Which part of the rocket returned to Earth?

3 How tall is the command module?

4 Why is the rocket so large compared with the command module?

5 How many hours did it take to reach the Moon?

Keywords

orbit

lunar module

G-force

18.2 Extreme sports

What forces act on falling objects?

Some people actually pay money to tie an **elastic** rope to their legs and jump off a bridge hundreds of feet in the air. They call it bungee jumping. Would you be prepared to do it?

Parachutes let people and things fall to the ground slowly so they are not hurt or damaged. Sometimes parachutes are used to drop food and machines to isolated areas.

The parachute collects air. The air pushes up. This is called **air resistance**. Air resistance balances some of the pull of gravity. The parachute slows down the person's fall.

Gravity pulls the parachutist downwards.

1 The bungee rope is loose. It does not pull on the jumper at all. **Gravity** pulls the jumper downwards.

2 The rope **stretches**. It is elastic and starts to pull on the jumper. When it is fully stretched it pulls the jumper back up.

Gravity pulls the jumper downwards.

3 At the top of the bounce the rope becomes slack again. It does not pull on the jumper. He starts to fall again.

Keywords

elastic

gravity

stretch

air resistance

Questions

1 What pulls the bungee jumper towards the ground?

2 What stops the bungee jumper hitting the ground?

3 Bungee ropes are elastic. What does 'elastic' mean?

4 If one parachute were twice the size of another, which one would land first?

5 What slows down parachutists as they fall towards the ground?

6 Does a long bungee have more stretch than a short one of the same thickness? Give a reason for your prediction.

18.3 Crumple zones

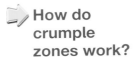

How do crumple zones work?

Modern cars have special areas that crumple like paper when they are involved in a crash. These areas are called **crumple zones** and save hundreds of lives every year. How do they do this?

When a car crashes into something the energy of the moving car has to go somewhere. If it passes straight to the passengers they are killed by the sudden **force**.

A steel cage around the passengers is very strong. This resists any forces left over from the crumple zones to keep the passengers safe.

If the crumple zones crumple they absorb some of the **energy**. The force bends the metal and so less is left over to pass to the passengers.

Air bags work in a similar way. When the car stops suddenly the air bag is filled with gas. The passengers hit the air bag not the hard dashboard. The bag deflates slightly when you hit it. This absorbs more of the energy in the collision.

Modern roads also help to protect people. Speed bumps and cameras force drivers to slow down. In a crash less damage is done if the car is travelling more slowly. Some roads even have special bends called chicanes built into them. Drivers have to slow down to get around these bends.

To work out the speed of a car road safety experts use this formula:

$$\text{Speed (mph)} = \frac{\text{distance travelled (m)}}{\text{time taken (hr)}}$$

For a car covering 12 miles in 15 minutes (0.25 hr):

$$\text{Speed} = \frac{12}{0.25} = 48 \text{ mph}$$

Questions

1 Why is a crumple zone softer than the passenger cage in a car?
2 Why is the passenger cage made of very strong steel?
3 List two ways air bags help to prevent injuries in a crash.
4 Why are road safety experts keen to reduce the speed of cars on city streets?
5 A car travels half a mile in 3 minutes. Is the driver breaking the 30 mph speed limit?

Keywords

crumple zones
force
energy
air bags

18.4 Thunderdome!

⇨ **How do forces make things move?**

This is the Thunderdome at The Burning Man Festival in Nevada, USA. Contestants are attached to **bungee** ropes hanging from the roof and then hit at each other with foam-covered bats. Not too many people get hurt!

bungee pulls the fighter up and the fighters weight **pulls** against it

the bungee rope tries to pull the heavy fighter upwards but his weight is too large

The swing is the key thing! If you swing round one way you end up going back the other! If you lose your balance your opponent gets you every time!

It's really strange. If you score a good hit with the stick your opponent moves but so do you – but in the opposite direction!

the heavier fighter is touching the floor. The floor pushes up against the fighter

the floor has no effect because the fighter is not touching it

I hate fighting someone who's so much bigger than me! It's much more difficult to get them to move!

Questions

1 What is the **force** pulling the fighters down towards the desert floor?

2 When is the bungee rope pulling hardest on the fighter?

3 Why does the fighter move backwards when he hits his opponent?

4 Will large fighters hang lower on the bungee ropes than small fighters?

5 How many people are watching? Estimate the total number of people watching from the metal dome.

Keywords

bungee

force

pulls

18 Data response: Play safe

Kids like excitement and strange things to climb over and swing on.
Parents like safety! How can the two agree?

When objects fall they gain energy. The energy
depends on:

- the size of the object (heavier objects gain more
  energy)
- the speed of the object (faster moving objects
  gain more energy).

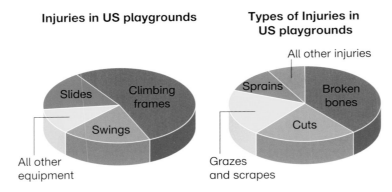

Injuries in US playgrounds

Types of Injuries in US playgrounds

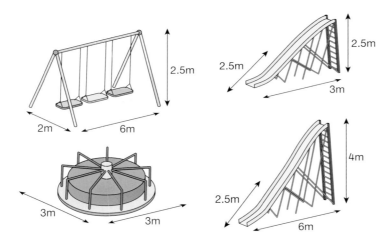

The speed of the object is affected by
how far it falls. When it starts falling it is
slow but as gravity pulls it downwards it
gets faster and faster.

Maximum safe height for a fall
All measurements are in centimetres

	Depth of surface coating		
	15	23	30
Bark mulch	180	300	330
Wood chips	180	210	360
Fine sand	150	150	270
Fine gravel	180	210	300

Data response

1. Which piece of playground equipment causes the most injuries?
2. What is the most common type of playground injury?
3. Why is a fall from a high climbing frame more serious than a fall from a low climbing frame?
4. A child falls 270 cm onto a layer of wood chips 30 cm deep. Will the child be hurt?
5. A climbing frame is 2 metres high. What depth of wood chips is needed to keep it safe?
6. How much wood chip will be needed beneath the play equipment shown in the plans for the new park?

7 The local council wants to ban one piece of play equipment in the park. Which one is it? Give reasons for your choice.

Research

8 A new type of lightweight plastic has been developed for safety helmets. Plan an investigation to compare the strength of this plastic with the old type.

Presentation

9 Prepare a presentation for kids to show them the dangers of some playground equipment. You must explain clearly about the dangers but not frighten them too much. Your presentation can use text, photographs, sounds and video. It will be sent to local schools on CD or DVD.

Learning progress

I know:

- Forces can be pulls, pushes, twists or bends. Forces are measured in Newtons. Unbalanced forces make things move.

- An increased force increases the length of an elastic material. Elastic materials can normally return to their original shape when the force is removed. If the force is too large the elastic material will be permanently damaged and will not return to its original shape. A stretched elastic band exerts a force.

- Gravity is a force pulling things towards the Earth. Weight is due to the force of gravity. Falling objects are acted on by gravity and drag (air resistance). Air resistance tends to slow down movement of falling objects.

- Rockets need very powerful engines to put things into space. Some parts of a rocket fall back to Earth after they have been used. These burn up in the atmosphere due to friction with the air.

- Falling objects have energy. The bigger the object and faster it is moving the more energy it has. Injuries in playgrounds are caused when children fall onto hard surfaces or are hit by moving objects. Soft surfaces under a climbing frame reduce the risk of injury if a child falls off it. Building smaller frames reduces the chance of injury.

- Large rockets are needed to put things in space. Some parts of some rocket shuttles return to Earth undamaged. Many objects burn up in the atmosphere as they fall back to Earth. Astronauts need to take air, food and special supplies with them. Space is very cold and silent.

I can:

- measure the speed of a moving object.

19.1 Eyes

 How do we see things?

We see things when **light** goes into our eyes. The photograph shows a fire juggler. The flames give out light which enters our eyes. The flames are **luminous**. This means they give out their own light. A light bulb and candle flame are also luminous objects.

Non-luminous objects cannot make their own light. They **reflect** the light made by something else. The walls of the building are non-luminous. We can only see them because they reflect light from the flames and the street light.

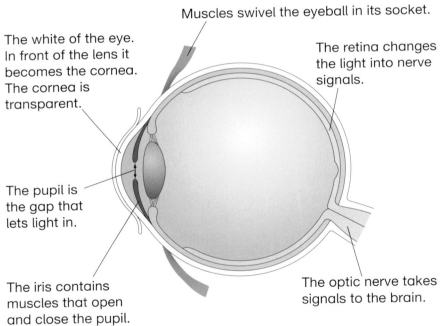

The white of the eye. In front of the lens it becomes the cornea. The cornea is transparent.

Muscles swivel the eyeball in its socket.

The retina changes the light into nerve signals.

The pupil is the gap that lets light in.

The iris contains muscles that open and close the pupil.

The optic nerve takes signals to the brain.

Questions

1 What does 'luminous' mean?
2 Name three things that are luminous.
3 What does 'non-luminous' mean?
4 Name three things that are non-luminous.
5 List the parts of the eye and explain what they do.
6 How could you prove to someone that light goes into your eyes?

Keywords

light
luminous
non-luminous
reflect

Let there be light!

19.2 Reflections

How do mirrors reflect light?

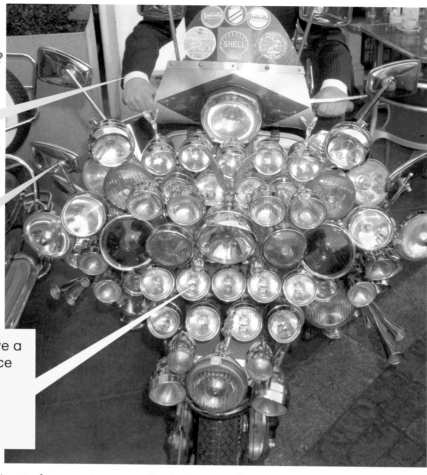

Light **reflects** off the biker's white shirt cuff in every direction. It looks the same from every direction.

The mirrors reflect light in a particular direction. This means you can see a clear **image** in a mirror.

The headlights have a curved silver surface to reflect the light forward. The curve helps to **focus** the **beam** of light.

We can use **rays** of light to investigate how mirrors reflect. A ray of light is a thin beam. We can see this beam when it touches a piece of white paper.

Mirrors are more complicated than they look. Mirror writing is writing that is the right way up but back to front – it makes no sense. But look at it in a mirror. The mirror flips the image, so the right side is on the left and the left on the right. Why is the word ambulance written the wrong way round in the picture?

Questions

1 What is the difference between the way in which a mirror and a piece of white paper reflect light?

2 Use a light beam to find out how mirrors reflect light. Try to predict in which direction the beam will bounce off the mirror.

3 Write your name in mirror writing. Check it with a mirror.

4 Draw a diagram to show how a flat mirror reflects a ray of light.

5 Think of at least two uses for curved mirrors.

Keywords

reflect

image

focus

beam

ray

19.3 Light rays

 How do lenses bend light?

Light travels in straight lines. We call a narrow beam of light a **light ray**. **Ray diagrams** show the way these beams of light reflect from a mirror or pass through a glass lens.

The substance the light rays pass through is called the **medium**. Air, glass and water are all good examples or **media** (the plural for medium). When light passes from one medium to another the ray is often bent into a new direction. **Lenses** use this bending to focus the light and make sharp, clear images.

Our brain has to interpret the light rays entering our eyes. Sometimes our brain makes things look bigger than they really are to make sense of the light rays going into our eyes. This is how the **convex** lens in a magnifying glass works.

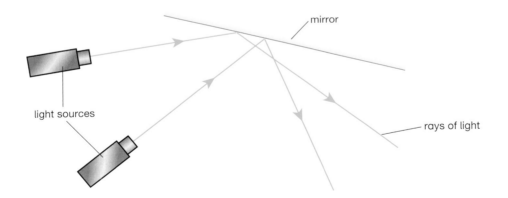

light sources

mirror

rays of light

Questions

1 What is a light ray?

2 What is the substance that light passes through called?

3 We do not say 'two mediums'. What is the correct plural word for medium?

4 Draw a ray diagram to show how a mirror reflects a light ray that hits it at 45°.

5 Draw a ray diagram to show how light from a near object passes through a convex lens.

Keywords

light ray

ray diagram

medium

media

lens

convex

19.4 Optical fibres

 How do optical fibres work?

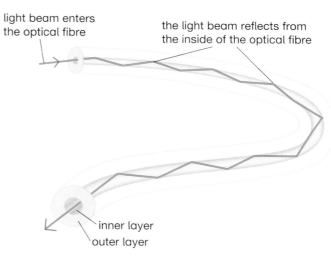

light beam enters the optical fibre

the light beam reflects from the inside of the optical fibre

inner layer
outer layer

Optical means 'to do with light'. Optical **fibres** carry light in the same way that water pipes carry water. How do they work?

When a beam of light hits a glass surface some passes straight through and some **reflects** back. In an optical fibre the beam bounces back into the middle of the fibre. This is called **total internal reflection**. Special glass can bend like a fibre but reflect like glass. In this way the light beam bounces along the fibre from side to side.

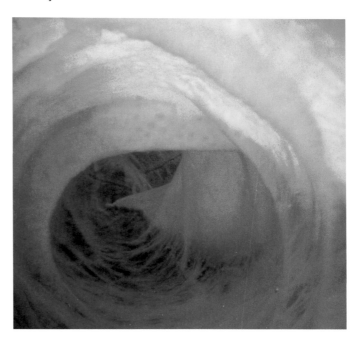

If you have a bundle of fibres each ray passes along a separate fibre. This means that the rays coming out are in the same position as the ones that entered. This means you can build a clear image. **Endoscopes** contain bundles of fibres to let you look inside the body. Messages can be coded into a series of flashes to pass along the fibre. Computers at each end of the fibre can code and decode the message.

Questions

1   What does the word 'optical' mean?

2   Why do endoscopes have fibres that carry light into the body as well as fibres that carry the image out?

3   Optical fibres can carry flashes of light. How can these be used to carry messages?

4   Plan an investigation to find out if the angle the light beam hits the glass surface affects how much is reflected.

Keywords

optical

fibre

reflect

total internal reflection

endoscope

19 Data response: Building a light show

This picture of Pink Floyd at the Live8 gig shows spotlights with light passing through solid plastic filters.

This picture of a gig in The Musician pub in Leicester shows white light projected through coloured oils. The light that passes through is coloured.

Spotlights used for the Live8 gig in Hyde Park on July 2nd 2005

Number of spotlights	Filters fitted	Power rating for each bulb (Watts)
85	red	3000
115	blue	3200
50	green	3200
50	purple	3200
100	yellow	3000
200	no filter	2500

Data response

1 List three of the coloured filters used for the Live8 gig.

2 What colour is the guitarist's shirt in the Leicester gig?

3 How can you tell that the guitarist's hat in the Leicester gig is not orange in colour?

4 How many red filters were used at the Live8 gig?

5 What is the total power of the blue spotlights at the Live8 gig?

6 What colour light was made by the spotlights with no filter fitted?

Research

7 A projector shows a film at a concert. The screen is 20 metres across. Plan an investigation to see how the distance from a projector affects the size of the image. Use your results to work out how far away from the screen the projector must be at the gig.

Presentation

8 Prepare a presentation for lighting engineers to show them how to make different coloured lights at a rock gig. You need to explain how to use filters and coloured bulbs to make a really good show. Your presentation should be made on a computer and saved to a disk so that it can be sent to lighting engineers all over the world.

Learning progress

I know:

● Luminous objects give out their own light but non-luminous objects only reflect light from other sources. We see things when light from them reaches the eye.

● The pupil allows light into the eye. It gets larger in dim light and smaller in bright light. The lens focuses a sharp image on the retina. The retina converts light to nerve signals that the brain can understand. The optic nerve carries these signals to the brain.

● Smooth shiny surfaces reflect light to give a clear reflection. The image in a mirror is the same way up and the same size as the object but the other way around.

● Rays of light travel in straight lines. Mirrors reflect light in straight lines. A lens or prism can bend the direction of the light ray.

● Sometimes light can be reflected from a transparent surface. This happens in optical fibres. Coded flashes of light can carry messages along an optical fibre at very high speed.

I can:

● Write a message in mirror writing.

● Draw a ray diagram to show the path of a ray of light along an optical fibre.

20.1 Solar system

What does the solar system contain?

The **solar system** includes the Sun at the centre and the nine **planets**. Planets further away from the Sun tend to take longer to circle around it than the planets close to its surface. The Earth is moving at about 67,000 miles per hour through space just to get round the Sun once every **year**!

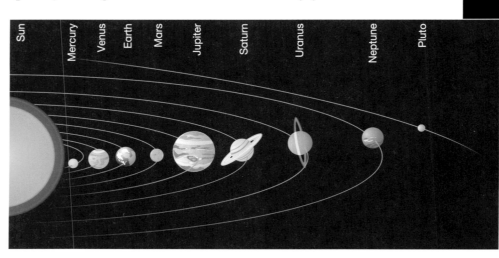

Planet	Distance from the Sun/ million km	Diameter/ km	Weight/ Earth = 1	Average temperature/ °C	Time round the Sun/year
Mercury	58	4969	0.05	510	0.24
Venus	108	12200	0.8	480	0.62
Earth	150	12757	1.0	15	1.00
Mars	228	6800	0.1	−50	1.88
Jupiter	779	143,600	318	−250	11.86
Saturn	1427	121,000	95	−180	29.46
Uranus	2670	47000	15	−220	84.0
Neptune	4496	44600	17	−200	164.8
Pluto	5906	3000	0.06	−240	247.7

Questions

1 What is at the centre of our solar system?
2 How many planets are there in our solar system?
3 Which planet is closest to the Sun?
4 Which is the largest planet?
5 Which planet has the lowest surface temperature?
6 Which planet is most like the Earth? Give reasons for your choice.

Keywords

solar system
planet
year
diameter
temperature

Watch this space

20.2 Sunshine – good or bad?

How do we know that sunlight contains energy?

Not the best thing about the Sun! When **ultraviolet** light hits our skin the **energy** speeds up certain chemical reactions. Some of these give us a tan. Some cause painful sunburn.

The sunlight is reflected onto the bottom of this kettle. It heats up for the world's most environmentally sound cup of tea!

This giant mirror outside Nottingham playhouse reflects the sky. When it was built people worried that it would **focus** the sunlight into a death 'ray'! This could fry pigeons flying into the beam!

The sun is a **star** – not even a particularly big one! There are billions of others in the universe. But to Earth the Sun is special. All the energy in the plants and animals on the planet comes from the **Sun**.

Questions

1 Give three ways we know that sunlight contains energy.
2 What is the name of the device that converts sunlight into electrical energy?
3 Why is a curved mirror sometimes used to collect solar energy?
4 Why is it dangerous to look straight up at the Sun?
5 How does a sundial work? Draw up a design for one. If you can – build it.

Keywords

ultraviolet

energy

focus

star

Sun

20.3 Satellites

What is a satellite?

A **satellite** is something moving around a **planet**. The Earth has one natural satellite and hundreds of artificial ones. The natural satellite is the Moon.

The Moon is a dead lump of rock measuring 3476 km across. It has no atmosphere. To survive here you need to take all your food, water and supplies with you. Only 12 men have ever set foot on the Moon. The picture shows the lunar rover – the only vehicle to drive on an Earth satellite!

Satcom 1 was launched in December 1975 and was one of the first geostationary satellites. A geostationary satellite orbits the Earth at exactly the same speed as the Earth turns. This means that it is always above the same spot on the planet. Geostationary satellites are used for communications. Satcom 1 was the first satellite to broadcast TV to all of the USA. It carried channels like ABC, NBC and CBS and many other cable channels. The UK's Sky Television did not begin until 1989 with the Astra satellite.

Artificial satellites

There are hundreds of satellites **orbiting** the Earth. These include:

- communications satellites for phones, radio and television
- weather forecasting
- telescopes that look out into space
- survey satellites that look down onto the Earth for scientific research
- military satellites.

Questions

1 What does the word 'satellite' mean?
2 What is the Earth's only natural satellite?
3 What is the diameter of the Moon?
4 Give three uses for artificial satellites.
5 Is the Earth the only planet with a moon?

Keywords

satellite

planet

orbit

20.4 Big mothers?

 How big is the universe?

Some people talk about the planet **Earth** as Mother Earth. The Earth is the mother to every one of the human beings living on it and is a big place. But how large is it compared with the universe?

Small objects

Object	Diameter/km
Planet Earth	12,757
The **Moon**	3,500
The Sun	1,390,000
The Solar System	30,000,000,000

Big objects

Object	Diameter/light years
The Solar System	0.0032
Our **galaxy** (the **Milky Way**)	160,000
The universe	156,000,000,000
1 light year = 10,000,000,000,000 km. That is the distance a ray of light travels in one year!	

It's difficult to imagine these sizes! So think of it in this way...

If the Sun was the size of a classroom the Earth would be as big as a grapefruit!

If the Solar System was the size of a classroom the Earth would be a grain of salt!

If our galaxy was the size of a classroom the Solar System would be ... too small to see!

There are over 100 billion stars in our galaxy. And there are probably 100 billion galaxies in the universe! Imagine you started counting stars and counted one every second. It would take about 3,200 years just to manage our galaxy even if you counted 24 hours a day with no holidays!

Questions

1. What is the **diameter** of the Earth?
2. What is the diameter of the Moon?
3. What is our galaxy called?
4. Why do we use light years to measure distances to stars and not kilometres?

Keywords

Earth
Moon
galaxy
Milky way
diameter

20 Data response: The space programme

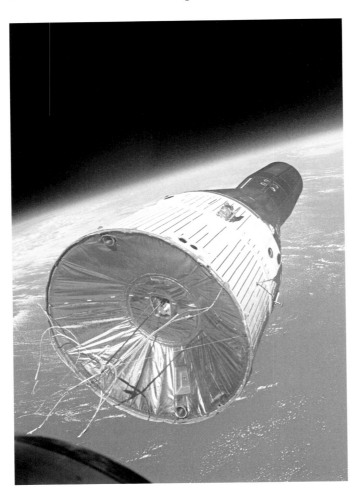

Gemini 7 spacecraft

Apollo 11

The early space race

Name	Launch date	Payload/ kg	Flight time	Notes
Sputnik 1	4 Oct 1957	84	92 days	First artificial satellite
Sputnik 2	3 Nov 1957	500	162 days	First living thing in space, a dog called Laika
Explorer 1	31 Jan 1958	14	60 days	First US satellite
Vostok 1	12 Apr 1961	4728	108 mins	First human being in space, Yuri Gagarin
Friendship 7	20 Feb 1962	1364	5 hours	First US astronaut
Vostok 6	16 Jun 1963	4728	2 days 23 hours	First woman in space, Valentina Tereshkova
Voshkod 2	18 Mar 1965	5695	26 hours	First space walk
Gemini 3	23 Mar 1965	3232	4 hours 53 mins	First US space walk
Apollo 7	11 Oct 1968	14 725	10 days 20 hours 9 mins	First successful Saturn V launch
Apollo 8	21 Dec 1968	28 962	6 days 3 hours	First men to pass around the Moon
Apollo 11	16 Jul 1969	43 961	8 days 2 hours 18 mins	First men to land on the Moon Neil Armstrong was the first man to walk on the Moon

Data response

1 When was Friendship 7 launched?

2 How much did Apollo 7 take into space?

3 Who was the first woman to go into space?

4 How long was the flight time for Vostok 1?

5 Draw a bar chart to show the rise in payloads for the Apollo missions.

6 Who was Laika?

Research

7 The surface of the Moon is covered with craters. These form when giant lumps of rock and ice called asteroids smash into the surface. But what decides how big a crater should be? Is it the size of the asteroid or the speed that it hits the surface? Plan an investigation to find out.

Presentation

8 We have hundreds of satellites flying over our heads every day. What are they used for? Prepare a presentation which shows what these satellites are used for. You can get images of many of these satellites from online libraries at NASA. Use these photographs to prepare an attractive illustrated presentation.

Learning progress

I know:

- The Sun is at the centre of our solar system. The Earth orbits the Sun. The Moon orbits the Earth. Eclipses occur when the Moon gets in the way of the light from the Sun. Artificial satellites orbiting the Earth are used for communication, spying and tracking.

- We can see planets and the Moon because they reflect light from the Sun. Other planets in our solar system also have moons. Planets take longer to orbit the Sun the further away they are from it.

- The universe contains many stars. The Sun is the one nearest to us. It can be dangerous to look at the Sun – especially through a telescope or binoculars. All stars start off as clouds of hydrogen which contract by gravity. A large star becomes a red giant, then a supernova and finally a black hole when it runs out of fuel.

I can:

- Draw a labelled picture of our solar system.

- List the things an astronaut needs to stay alive.

21.1 Energy sources and uses

 Where can we get our energy supplies?

A solar powered bicycle! Probably not really suitable for the M25 though! And you need to clean that **solar panel** at the back regularly.

Energy is needed to get things done. Energy makes people and machines work. Different things get their energy from different **energy sources**. People get their energy from the food they eat. Machines get energy from fuel or electricity. Some farms in Australia have their own electricity **generators**, which run on oil or wind power. In North Africa they use wood and animal dung for fuel.

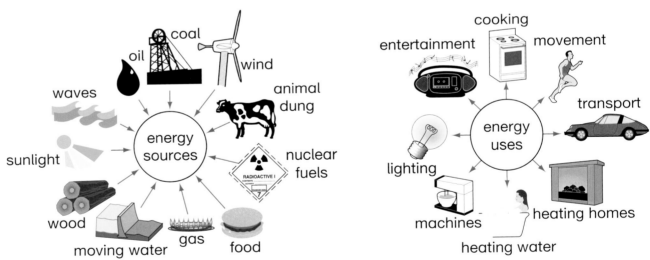

Questions

1 List all of the energy sources mentioned on this page.
2 Sort the list into those you use and those you do not use.
3 Why is bottled gas useful when you go camping?
4 Why do you think that there are no gas or electricity supplies to remote areas?
5 List five ways your life would change if you had no electricity.

Keywords

solar panel
energy
energy source
generator

21.2 Non-renewable energy sources

What is a non-renewable energy source?

Miners like these have been working in mines for hundreds of years to collect coal for us to use at home and at work. Coal, oil and gas are called **fossil fuels**. They were made millions of years ago and are found underground. Fossil fuels are useful because they release **energy** when they burn.

Uranium is another fuel that is found underground. We use it in nuclear power stations to produce electricity. Fossil fuels and uranium are non-renewable. **Non-renewable** fuels are fuels which cannot be replaced. We will eventually run out of non-renewable fuels.

Years of known fossil fuel reserves left at current rates of consumption

Fuel	Years left
Oil	40.5
Gas	66.7
Coal	164

Questions

1 What does 'non-renewable' mean?
2 List four non-renewable fuels.
3 Which non-renewable fuels do you use at home?
4 Why can burning fuel be bad for the environment?
5 Give two reasons why it is difficult to predict when fossil fuels will run out.

Keywords
fossil fuel

energy

uranium

non-renewable

21.3 Renewable energy sources

 What are renewable energy sources?

In 2005 the 101 **wind farms** in the UK produced enough **electricity** to power 550,000 homes. If this power had been made by traditional power stations it would have made over two million tonnes of carbon dioxide and 26 tonnes of poisonous sulphur dioxide gas. Most wind farms are located in remote areas because they take up a lot of space and can be noisy.

Energy can be created from wind, waves, tides and the Sun. None of these energy sources will run out as long as the Earth exists. These are **renewable** energy sources. The Sun can be used to heat things directly and wind can be used to turn machinery. Most renewable energy sources are used to make electricity and do not cause **pollution**.

Photocells or solar cells make electricity when light falls on them. They are useful in areas that are a long way from the mains. This sign is designed for bendy roads in mountains of Tibet. The symbol means 'Watch out!'. Solar cells produce small amounts of electricity and need a battery to store energy for when it is dark.

Wood is the fuel that humans have used longer than any other. It is a **biomass** fuel. This means it is produced by living things. Because trees can grow to replace the ones we cut down to burn it is a renewable fuel. Other renewable fuels include a kind of diesel oil made from soya beans and even alcohol made from sugar cane!

Questions

1 List three renewable energy sources.
2 What do you use in school that is run on solar power?
3 List the advantages of renewable energy sources.
4 Give two disadvantages of wind farms.
5 Plan an investigation to find out if a windmill with three blades produces more electricity than a windmill with two.

Keywords

wind farm

electricity

energy

renewable

pollution

biomass

The burning question

21.4   Fire wise or flame foolish?

What is the best way to put out a fire?

Jet cars – from standing still to over 300mph in under five seconds! Great fun but a real fire risk! How could you protect mechanics and drivers from a 12 foot long flame where your exhaust should be?

To burn something needs three things: **fuel**, **heat** and **oxygen**. The **fire triangle** shows this. If any one is missing the flame goes out. The easiest way to stop the jet engine burning is to switch off the fuel.

heat   fuel   air/oxygen

Fire fighters use **extinguishers** to put out fires. They need to choose the right extinguisher for each job because the wrong one can sometimes make things worse.

Carbon dioxide cylinder

This pushes the oxygen away from the flame. It also takes away the heat. Good for all sorts of fires.

Water Fire extinguisher

Keeps oxygen from the flame and cools it down. Good for wood and paper fires. Do not use on oil or electrical fires!

Powder extinguisher

Keeps oxygen away from the flame. Good for electrical fires.

Questions

1   What three things do you need to start a fire?

2   Which sort of extinguisher could you use for a bonfire that has got out of control?

3   Which sort of extinguisher should you not use on electrical fires?

4   Some people throw a pile of sand on burning oil. Why?

5   What sort of extinguishers should they keep at the jet car race track? Why?

Keywords

fuel

heat

oxygen

fire triangle

extinguisher

21 Data Response: Designing wind turbines

Windmills are ways to capture energy from the wind. They can be used to grind corn, lift water or generate electricity. These windmills are on a farm in Cornwall and produce enough electricity to supply over 4,000 homes every year. To produce electricity the turning blade turns a generator.

The approximate power output for a single blade windmill

Diameter of blade (m)	Wind speed (m sec⁻¹)	Approx power output (kW)
7	5	1531
5	5	781
3	5	281
1	5	31
7	10	12250
5	10	6250
3	10	2250
1	10	250
7	15	41343
5	15	21094
3	15	7594
1	15	8434
7	20	98000
5	20	50000
3	20	18000

Output from wind generators

Number of turns	Strength of magnet	Power produced
1000		
2000		
3000		
4000		
5000		
1000		
2000		
3000		
4000		
5000		

Data response

1 How much power would a 3m windmill produce in a wind of 10 m/sec?

2 How much power would a 7m windmill produce in a wind of 5 m/sec?

3 The average windspeed in Harlech, North Wales is 5 m/sec. How much energy would a 5m windmill produce?

4 What two things could you do to a windgenerator to increase the power output? (You are not allowed to just increase the windspeed!)

5 Draw a graph to show the increase in power for an aerogenerator with a blade diameter of 7m if the windspeed increases from 0 to 20 m/sec.

6 Does a windmill with two blades generate twice as much power as one with only one blade? Plan an investigation to find out.

7 People like electricity! It powers their televisions, lights their houses and makes their iPods work! But generating electricity costs money and damages the environment. Design a presentation to show people why we need to find new ways to generate electricity in the future. Make sure you answer all of these questions in your presentation:

- What do we use electricity for?
- How can we generate electricity?
- Why are non-renewable fuels like coal, gas and oil a problem?
- How could we cut down our need for electricity?

Learning progress

I know:

- A photocell uses light energy to make electricity. Photocells are useful sources of electricity for small devices and remote locations.
- Photocells do not produce pollution when they are in use. They have no moving parts to wear out. They do not run out while the Sun is shining. Photocells are quite expensive and do not produce large amounts of electricity. They need to be quite large to produce much electricity.
- Light from the Sun is reflected to a focus by a curved mirror.
- When light is absorbed by a surface, light energy is transferred to heat energy.
- Windows can let light into a house to provide passive solar heating.
- Energy is needed to do useful things. We get energy from a variety of sources. The Sun is a stable source of energy.
- Some energy sources are non-renewable, for example coal, oil, gas and uranium. These energy sources will run out.
- A fuel is something that burns to give out useful light or heat. Good fuels produce a lot of heat, burn easily, produce very little pollution and are easy to control.
- Some energy sources are renewable, for example wind, sunlight, waves. These are produced all the time and will not run out. Renewable energy sources all depend on the Sun. Biomass can be a renewable source of heat energy.
- A wind turbine uses energy from the wind to generate electricity.

I can:

- Draw a poster to show the fire triangle.
- Tell others what the school fire drill is.

acid	a chemical that turns litmus paper red; it can often dissolve things that water cannot
adaptation	a feature of a living organism that helps it to survive, e.g. the zebra's stripes are an adaptation that makes them difficult to see in the wild and so protects them from predators
addictive	people are addicted to something if they would suffer if it was removed; in psychological addiction the suffering is mental e.g. people can be very bad tempered or fidgety if they give up cigarettes, physical addiction occurs with drugs like heroin
afterbirth	the placenta which is delivered after the baby has been born
air	the mixture of gases in the atmosphere
air resistance	the force air exerts on an object moving through it; air resistance slows down movement and increases as the moving object gets faster
air sac	another name for the alveolus at the end of the thin tubes in the lungs
airways	spaces that let air move through them
alkali	a substance which makes a solution that turns red litmus paper to blue
alloy	a mixture of two or more metals
alum	a white crystal that dissolves in water
aluminium	a shiny metal; it is very light in weight
amalgam	an alloy that contains mercury
analogue	a signal that shows a complete range of frequencies
animal testing	testing chemicals on animals to see if they are dangerous
antenatal	before birth
Apatosaurus	a plant-eating dinosaur
artificial	made by human beings
asthma	an illness that stops people breathing properly – it often affects children
atmosphere	the mixture of gases we call the air; the atmosphere is about 80% nitrogen and 20% oxygen with other gases making up less than 1%
atria	the two thin-walled chambers at the top of the heart
azurite	a coloured mineral containing the metal copper
bandages	strips of cloth used to bind up wounds
battery	a device that changes chemical energy into electrical energy
beam	a ray of light
bicarbonate of soda	sodium hydrogen carbonate; it breaks down when heated to give off carbon dioxide and leave sodium carbonate
biomass	a biomass fuel is a fuel made from growing plants, e.g. wood, straw and alcohol
blood pressure	the pressure of blood in your arteries and veins
borax	a chemical sometimes used to flameproof fabrics
breathing	moving air into and out of the lungs; breathing is sometimes called respiration although the word respiration is also used for a chemical process going on in all living cells not just in the lungs
bronchiole	a thin tube in the lungs leading from the bronchi to the air sacs
bronchus	the tubes leading from the bottom of the trachea into the lungs; humans have two bronchi, one for each lung
bungee	another name for an elastic rope
carbon dioxide	a gas containing only carbon and oxygen; its chemical formula is CO^2
carbonate	compounds containing the carbonate group of atoms; the carbonate group formula is CO^3

catalytic converter	boxes fitted to vehicle exhausts which reduce the level of nitrogen oxides and unburnt hydrocarbons in the exhaust fumes
cell membrane	the thin layer around the outside of a cell
chemical reaction	a change that occurs when a number of substances react together to produce new substances
circulation	moving substances around a body; the blood system in humans is sometimes called the circulatory system
cobalt	a shiny metal
cochineal	a red dye made from beetles
code	a code is a way to represent a message
coil	a spiral, often made of wire; coils are often used in electrical circuits to magnetise metal objects
coma	a state of deep unconsciousness
compass	a magnetic needle that moves freely to always point North-South
composite	a substance made of two or more different substances mixed together
contraction	to get smaller or shorter
convex	wider in the middle than at the edges
copper	a yellowy-orange metal
corrosion	rust
cytoplasm	the material in the cell inside the cell membrane but outside the nucleus
decay	to rot
decode	to get the original message from a coded message
density	a measure of how heavy something is
detergent	detergents do the same job as soaps
diabetes	a disease caused by the failure to control blood sugar levels due to the inability of the pancreas to secrete insulin
diameter	a straight line across a circle that passes through the centre
diaphragm	a flat layer of muscle just below the lungs that helps with breathing in and out
digestion	the breaking down of large food particles or molecules into smaller particles or molecules which the body can absorb
digital	a code that depends on on-off signals
donor	someone who gives an organ for transplant
ejaculation	sudden release of sperm
elastic	stretchy, elastic materials can return to their original size and shape after they have been subjected to a force
electricity	a form of energy involving charges flowing along a conductor
electrolyte	the liquid carrying the electric current in an electric cell
electromagnet	a coil of copper wire, often surrounding an iron bar, that produces a magnetic field when electricity flows though the copper wire
electroplating	covering something with a layer of metal using electricity
enamel	the hard outer coating of the teeth
encode	to convert a message into a code
energy	energy is the ability of a system to do something; we detect energy by the effect it has on the things around us – heating them up, moving them, etc.
energy source	wind, waves and fossil fuels are all examples of energy sources
engine	a machine that can produce movement from another energy source
environment	all the things around us
enzymes	special proteins found in living organisms that speed up the rate of a chemical reaction

evidence	evidence includes all the results and data collected from investigations; people should agree about evidence even if they disagree about what a piece of evidence means
evolution	the gradual change in living organisms over millions of years
excretion	getting rid of wastes made by the body – all living things must do this
extinct	a species is extinct when all members of the species have died
extinguisher	something that can put out a fire
faeces	the solid waste from our gut
fats	a type of food that is very rich in energy – fats are found in chocolate, butter and margarine and the fat on bacon and other meats
fermentation	breakdown of food by microorganisms that does not require oxygen
fertilises	makes something grow
fibre	a hair or thin strand of something, e.g. wool is made of fibres
fire triangle	fuel, heat and oxygen are the three parts of the fire triangle
flameproof	something that does not catch fire easily
focus	the point at which light rays met up to form a clear image
force	a force is a push or pull which is able to change the velocity or shape of a body
fossil	preserved evidence of a dead animal or plant; fossils can be body parts or evidence of activity like tracks, burrows, nests or teethmarks
fossil fuel	a fuel like coal, oil and natural gas formed by the decay of dead living things over millions of years
fuel	something that gives out energy, usually as light and heat, when it burns.
galaxy	a large collection of stars; our galaxy is called the Milky Way
gas	all substances are solids, liquids or gases; a gas has no fixed shape and will expand to fill all of the space available in the container where it is stored
generator	A device for converting energy of movement (kinetic energy) into electrical energy (current flow)
genitals	the sexual organs visible outside the body, e.g. the penis and testes of males
glucose	a type of sugar – glucose is sometimes called dextrose
graphite	a type of carbon often used in pencils as the 'lead'
gravity	the force of attraction between two bodies caused by their mass; the force of gravity produced by a body depends on its mass: the larger the mass the larger the force
heartbeat	the sound of the muscles of the heart contracting to push blood through the body
host	an organism that is carrying another one inside its body
hybrid	an organism made when two different species breed together
hydrochloric acid	an acid formed when hydrogen chloride gas (HCl) dissolves in water
hypothermia	an illness caused by the body getting too cold
Ichthyosaurus	an extinct type of reptile that used to live in the water and looked a bit like a fish
image	a pattern of light that our brain can interpret; you can see images projected onto screens or reflected in a mirror or glass
indicator	a chemical that changes colour in acid and alkaline solutions; indicators are used to find out the pH of a solution
indigestion	not being able to digest something – sometimes called stomach ache
indigo	a blue dye
infection	an illness caused by microorganisms
inhaler	a way to get a drug into the lungs; often used by people with asthma

inject	to push something into something else; often used to deliver drugs through the skin with a sharp hollow needle
insulin	a hormone secreted by cells in the pancreas; insulin encourages cells to take up glucose and so reduces blood sugar levels
internal environment	the conditions inside a living organism, e.g. the temperature or levels of sugar in the blood
interpret	you interpret the results from an investigation by explaining what they show about your original idea
iron	a grey metal
Jurassic	an era from about 210 to 140 million years ago
kidney	your two kidneys make urine to get rid of waste products from the blood
kilowatt-hour	the units used to measure electricity supplied to a device
labour	the contractions of the uterus that lead to birth
large intestine	a part of the gut near the bottom – it absorbs water from digested food
lead	a dark grey soft metal
lens	a piece of glass that can change the direction of light rays
Leukaemia	a serious type of blood disease
life process	something that is true about all living things, e.g. respiration or excretion
light	a form of energy that allows us to see objects. Light is given out by hot objects like the Sun and the filament in an electric bulb
light ray	a beam of light, often used in diagrams to show how the light moves through lenses and bounces off mirrors
lime	a white powder that makes an alkali when it dissolves in water
limewater	a solution of calcium hydroxide in water; limewater goes milky white when carbon dioxide dissolves in it
litmus paper	paper containing litmus dyes; it turns red in acid and blue in alkaline solutions
luminous	glowing; some insects are luminous and glow in the dark to attract a mate
lunar module	the part of the Apollo spacecraft that landed on the Moon
lung capacity	the amount of air you can hold in your lungs
magnetic	an object that is magnetic is attracted by a magnet
malachite	a green copper-containing mineral
medium	the name given to the material that electromagnetic radiation is passing through
mercury	a liquid, silver-coloured metal
metal	a substance that is shiny when pure, can be beaten into sheets or drawn into wires; metals usually have quite high melting points and conduct heat and electricity well
meths	another name for methanol – a poisonous alcohol often used to dissolve substances like paints and inks
mobile	able to be moved
moon	the Earth's natural satellite (also the largest!)
mordant	a chemical which helps a dye to stick to a fabric
Morse	a type of code using dots and dashes
musk	a natural product from the musk deer which is used to make perfume
natural	something that has not been made by human beings
neutral	a neutral solution has a pH of 7 and is neither acid nor alkaline
neutralisation	a reaction between an acid and an alkali to produce a neutral solution
nickel	A hard, silvery-white metal that does not corrode quickly; some expensive cars use nickel instead of steel to prevent rusting

nicotine	the addictive drug found in tobacco
nitrogen	a non-reactive gas that makes up most of the atmosphere
nitrogen oxides	gases formed when nitrogen burns in air; nitrogen oxides dissolve in water to make acids
non-luminous	something that does not make its own light
non-renewable	non-renewable fuels are not being made fast enough at the moment and so will run out at some point in the future
North Pole	the point that the North-seeking pole of a magnet points towards
nucleus	the control centre of the cell; the nucleus is surrounded by a membrane that separates it from the rest of the cell – many microorganisms do not have a proper nucleus
oils	fatty chemicals
optical	to do with light
orbit	the path a satellite takes around a planet
ore	a rock containing valuable minerals
ovary	the part of the female body that produces the egg
oxygen	a colourless gas with no smell that makes up about 20% of the air
paint	a mixture of pigments and medium used to add colour to an object
paraffin	a type of fuel made from oil; it can also be used s a solvent for some paints and dyes
particulates	small specks of something, often used to describe the soot coming from vehicle exhausts
penis	the organ in males that is used in sexual intercourse and carries urine out of the body
petrol	a fuel made from oil and used to power road vehicles
pH scale	the range of levels of acidity or alkalinity; a pH of 7 is neutral, a pH below 7 is acid and the lower it goes the more acid it becomes, a pH above 7 is alkaline
pigment	chemicals which absorb certain wavelengths of light and so look coloured
planet	a large body moving around a star; we live on the planet Earth that is moving around a star we call the Sun
pollutant	a chemical that causes pollution
pollution	chemicals made by human activity that are damaging to the environment
population	a group of organisms of the same type living in the same area
power	the rate that a system transfers energy; power is usually measured in watts (W) (a system with a power rating of 1 watt transfers 1 joule of energy per second)
pressure	the force acting on a surface divided by the area of the surface; it is measured in newtons per square metre (N/m^2)
preventer	a drug that prevents asthma attacks
product	something made by a chemical reaction
protector	a drug that protects the body against the damaging effects of some illnesses, e.g. asthma
protein	a food chemical found in meat, eggs and fish; protein is used to build muscles
pump	a device to push a liquid along a tube; pumps can move liquids either by sucking on them or pushing on them
radiation	energy that travels as light
ray diagram	a way to show how rays of light pass through a medium
reactant	a chemical taking part in a chemical reaction

recycling	turning wastes into useful materials
reflect	to bounce something back – usually light from a mirror or sound from a solid wall
rejection	rejection occurs when the body's immune system fights against foreign chemicals; it is a particular problem in transplants when the body can destroy the organ that has been transplanted into it to make it better
renewable	windpower, wave power and solar power are all examples of renewable sources of energy
resources	things in the environment we use to make things
respiration	the chemical process that makes energy from food in the cells in your body; all living things must respire
respond	something an animal does as a result of a stimulus, e.g. the pupil in the eye responds to bright light by getting smaller
rust	brown crystals that form on iron or steel exposed to damp air
satellite	a body orbiting around a larger body; communications satellites orbit the Earth to relay messages from mobile phones
shiver	small movements of muscles that produce warmth when you feel cold
signal	the part of the message that contains the important information
small intestine	part of the gut; the small intestine is very long and absorbs digested food into the body
soap	a chemical that helps with washing
solar panel	a device that converts sunlight into electricity
solder	an alloy that melts at a low temperature and is used to make connections in some electrical circuitboards
solute	a solid that dissolves in a liquid
solution	something formed when a solute dissolves in a liquid
solvent	the liquid that dissolves a solute to make a solution
sound	a form of energy that we can hear; sound is actually tiny movements of particles in the air
South Pole	the point that the south-seeking pole of a magnet points towards
species	a group of living things; humans belong to the species Homo sapiens
sperm	special cells produced by the male; sperm joins with an egg from a female to produce a baby
steam distillation	passing steam through something to drive off useful chemicals
steel	an alloy of iron and carbon; steel is stronger than iron and does not rust so quickly
stitches	thread that holds the edges of a wound together while it heals
stomach	part of your gut; it helps to digest protein
sugar	white sweet-tasting crystals
sulphur dioxide	a poisonous gas made when sulphur burns in air or oxygen; many fossil fuels like coal and oil contain small amounts of sulphur so produce sulphur dioxide when they burn
swamp	very wet areas of ground
sweat	liquid produced by the skin; it cools you down when it evaporates
tar	a black, sticky liquid that smokers take into their lungs when they smoke a cigarette
terminal	one end of a battery
thermochromic	a pigment that changes colour when it gets hotter or colder
tin	a shiny grey metal
tobacco	the dried leaves of the plant Nicotiana; people smoke tobacco in cigarettes, cigars or pipes

total internal reflection	reflection of a ray of light back into a piece of glass when it reaches the edge
toxic	poisonous
transplant	to put an organ from one organism into another
trichloroethane	a solvent used to clean paint and ink from objects
turmeric	a yellow food dye often used in curries
Tyrannosaurus Rex	a meat-eating dinosaur
unit	a unit of electricity is the way the electricity company measures how much you have used – and have to pay!
universal indicator	an indicator that changes colour in solutions of different pHs
uranium	a radioactive metal used in nuclear power stations and bombs
urine	liquid made by your kidneys to get rid of wastes from the blood
vagina	the tube leading from the base of the uterus to the outside of a woman's body
valves	something that only lets liquids pass one way
ventricles	large muscular chambers in the heart
voltage	the measure of how much electrical current a battery can push through an electric circuit
water	a clear liquid found in all living things; water contains the elements hydrogen and oxygen and has the chemical formula H_2O
waterproof	does not let any water pass through
water-resistant	something that reduces the amount of water that passes through it
weave	the way threads are arranged together to make a fabric
weight	the force of gravity acting on a body on the Earth; since weight is a force it is measured in newtons (people often use the word weight to mean mass but this is not strictly correct)
weld	to join two metals together by melting them
white spirit	a solvent used to clean paint and ink from objects
wind farm	a collection of wind generators
windproof	a fabric that does not let wind pass through it
womb	the uterus in the female where the baby grows before birth
yarn	another name for thread
year	the time it takes the Earth to travel around the Sun